1966

MYSTERIES

OF THE ISLANDS

ROBERT DE LA CROIX

Translated from the French by
ANNE CARTER

The John Day Company
New York

FIRST AMERICAN EDITION, 1961

© 1960 BY FREDERICK MULLER LTD.

Library of Congress Catalogue Card
Number: 60-15744

MANUFACTURED IN THE UNITED STATES OF AMERICA

Contents

MYSTERIES
OF THE ISLANDS

1

Mysteries of the Islands

"LAND ahead!"

The men on watch jumped at the sudden, unexpected cry from the masthead. It was a clear July night in the year 1890 and the *Federation*, a three-master out of Nantes, was on her way from Saigon to pick up a cargo of copra in the Philippines.

"He's dreaming. We're two hundred and fifty miles from land," said the lieutenant, but he reached automatically for his glass. "Of course there's nothing there," he added, and sent for the lookout.

The *Federation* was on her maiden voyage, but it had begun badly when she ran aground on shallows off Billiton in the Java Sea, and later, at Saigon, a sudden squall had driven her onto the riverbank. The *Federation* had been floated off and was able to continue her voyage the next day, but the accidents had made a deep impression on her crew and left some of them wondering how many more disasters lay in store for them before they saw France again.

"But, sir, I swear I saw an island right ahead, at least I thought I saw it," insisted the lookout.

"You are aware the nearest land is two hundred and fifty miles away?"

Not daring to answer, the sailor was returning to his post when the lieutenant called him back.

"No, stay here, you may have more hallucinations."

Another man was sent aloft to replace him and once again there was peace aboard the *Federation*. Occasionally the lieutenant's voice could be heard giving an order to change course, then there was silence again, broken only by the familiar sounds of wind in the shrouds, creaking blocks and groaning timbers.

Twenty minutes went by. The lieutenant raised his glass and scanned the horizon, then he returned to his favorite corner of the bridge which he only left to pace the deck quietly smoking his pipe. Scarcely had he propped himself comfortably against the rail than a shiver ran through him as the cry went up again from the masthead:

"Land ahead!"

Such was their sense of impending danger that the men turned instinctively not to the sea but toward their officer. Twice had come that warning voice announcing something that should have been, that surely must be, impossible: an island had appeared in the open sea in latitudes where all the charts were blank.

"It could be a mirage, sir," hazarded one of the men.

"Up to the masthead with you. Tell me if you can see it too."

There was always the possibility of a mirage, or the black shape of a vessel without lights, or even a drifting hulk. . . .

"Land ahead!"

The same cry, fantastic and unbelievable as it was, rang out from the lookout, and the startled helmsman swung the wheel suddenly to port.

The lieutenant's hands were sweating slightly as he gripped the glass. His mind refused to register the facts. He must be insane, but looming through the darkness dead ahead he could make out a black line ridged with what appeared to be trees. He struggled to believe it was the result of some kind of collective hallucination, for there was no land there, there couldn't be. He held the butt of his telescope more closely to his eye, as if that would help him see more clearly. Land . . . an island . . . the words danced defiantly in his brain, as if they were telling him, "So you wouldn't believe it. Well, now let's see what you have to say to this."

"What's going on here?"

The lieutenant turned and saw Soulas, master of the *Federation*, standing behind him, still buttoning his overcoat, his cap hastily rammed onto uncombed hair and his face heavy with sleep.

"Sir, it's . . . that is, I think . . ."

"Speak up, man."

The lieutenant took a deep breath, like a man who knows he's talking nonsense, and muttered rapidly, "An island, sir."

Soulas snatched the telescope and his face set grimly as his fingers tightened on the brass tube.

"How do you explain land two hundred and fifty miles out at sea, sir? It hardly seems possible. I've considered the likelihood of a mirage or a navigational error. The compass may be wild, of course."

The lieutenant was speaking very fast, as if he were trying to ignore the absurdity of his own suggestions. Soulas checked the officer's flood of words.

"We're well on our course and I don't believe in visions. Not when the sky's as clear as this. It's land all right."

"But that's fantastic," sighed the lieutenant.

Soulas shrugged. Their present concern was with the facts, not with understanding them, and there was no doubt that the island was a fact. Time enough later to find out if there was anything peculiar or unnatural about its appearance; for the present the only problem was to avoid being wrecked on its coast, still some miles distant. He gave the order to alter course 90° to port and called all hands on deck to shorten sail. *Federation*'s speed dropped and she sailed slowly along the coast of the mysterious island.

"A volcanic eruption?" suggested the lieutenant.

"I've thought of that," said Soulas. "But in that case there'd be no trees."

Yet trees there were, jutting into the pale night sky and standing out clearly in the eye of the telescope. Every man on board was awake and hanging over the starboard rails, staring at a sight that might have been a continuation of their interrupted dreams. Voices echoed round the ship: "Land. . . . Can you see it?" . . . "An island." . . . "Know what it's called?" and the murmurs from the deck served to emphasize the silence on the bridge where the officers were cudgeling their brains for an answer to the riddle rising out of the dark sea.

One thing had been established: the ship was dead on her course. The compass had been checked and an estimate of the ship's speed made from the log. Furthermore, reference to books on navigation had positively confirmed that no land, or anything that might be taken for land, had ever been sighted in these latitudes, which were too well frequented to leave any possibility of new discoveries. Every year the *Federation*'s course was followed by hundreds of vessels, under steam and sail, and none of them had ever recorded a sight of land.

Yet the black mass was there, close by and patently real.

"Well, gentlemen, I believe we should delay no further. I will put in a report. . . ."

"Land ahead!"

An uneasy silence fell on deck, the ominous hush that greets the threat of the unknown. In the first place the island should now have been on the starboard bow and not dead ahead, and secondly the lookout's warning was superfluous since the eyes of every man on board were riveted on it. But how could he be blamed when the whole crew were plunged in such an atmosphere of mystery that even the tiny, familiar noises of a sailing ship seemed strangely different, and the structure of yards and rigging seemed to melt into the uneasy shapes of another world beyond men's reason?

"Another island," said Soulas with a strained laugh. "You'd think we were in the midst of a phantom archipelago."

His smile vanished and his face set again in worried lines as he and his officers peered into the darkness that lay like a thick curtain before them.

Then things happened quickly. Two terrific blows shook the vessel and the black curtain parted. Still nothing could be distinguished at first, as if the darkness had only given way to greater darkness. A tearing groan burst from the framework of the hull and this was drowned by a succession of strange, harsh noises, like the shrieks of the weird denizens of some phantasmal world into which the bark had stumbled.

Above the deck of the ship in mid-ocean a tree suddenly appeared, rose slowly in the air and fell with a crash of rending timbers onto the fo'c'stle. Another in full leaf towered over the mizzenmast, sending a shower of soil onto the deck, and the resinous smell of smashed and splintered wood began to fill the sea air as though a forest had put to sea.

Soulas had instinctively given the order hard to starboard but too late to prevent her striking. Now his ship was held fast, a prisoner of the unknown isle.

Dazed by the shock, the men stared uncomprehendingly at the branches tangled in their shrouds until the officers set them to the tasks of clearing the deck and inspecting the hull for leaks. The mystery was only deepened when soundings were taken and the lead did not touch bottom. Although it was less than two hundred yards long, the islet appeared to rest on a base dropping sheer into the sea.

A boat was lowered to investigate the possibilities of freeing the ship and it was found that the damage was less serious than had been feared. Her bows had been lifted about a dozen yards, but with a little wind the vessel could be floated off.

"We'll have a try at dawn," said Soulas.

The rest of the night dragged by in an endless, agonized vigil. None of the sailors could sleep and they strolled about the deck talking in low voices, to the accompaniment of uneasy creakings from the ship as the water, sucking greedily along her hull, seemed to turn her into a hostile stranger.

The long period of waiting left each man a prey to his own fears, although the general feeling was that there was not much actual danger from running aground, but the men felt trapped at the mercy of an unknown power, some strange force that had placed the islands so inexplicably across the *Federation*'s course.

At last dawn spread over the sea, but daylight only served to increase the crew's uneasiness. While it was still dark the illusion of a nightmare could be sustained but the light pitilessly showed them reality, that two mysterious islands had appeared in the sea and that one of them held the three-master captive.

Soulas ordered a pair of boats to be manned and lowered to make an attempt to tow the bark off stern first. Encouraging shouts greeted each effort as the men saw the cables tighten, but the bows remained immovable.

When the sun rose a breeze sprang up, and Soulas determined to take advantage of the slightest puffs of wind. After the men in the boats had been toiling for two hours, a triumphant shout went up; the bows had shifted almost a yard. Heartened by success the boats' crews strained harder than ever at their oars, muscles bulging and faces lined with fatigue, and at last, a little after midday, the *Federation* floated clear; and slowly, under a heavy sky that turned the sea to lead, the two islands disappeared below the horizon.

On arrival in the Philippines Soulas at once reported his strange discovery, but the survey department declared categorically that no land had ever been sighted in the latitudes reported by the French captain. Other seamen listened to the stories of the *Federation*'s crew with amused disbelief, clearly convinced that they had experienced some sort of collective hallucination.

Soulas made no attempt to argue his point, but he made up his mind to set his course past the islands again on the return journey and plot their exact position. Two days out, when he should have sighted the phantom islands, he could see nothing. Although the *Federation* circled the empty ocean for six hours it was without success; the islands had vanished.

Greatly as he desired an explanation of the mystery, Soulas did not persist. It was not in his power to order the ship off her course and so, very reluctantly, he resumed his voyage southward.

The *Federation*'s career was not a long one. Six years after the events recorded she again foundered on an island, this time only too real. On February 20, 1896, she was driven by a cyclone onto the low, deserted coast of Providence Island to the northeast of Madagascar and went to pieces. Her crew managed to get ashore and subsisted on the island for several weeks, living on wild figs and shellfish, until they were rescued by a passing ship.

Superstitious seamen maintained her grounding on the mysterious isles to be a premonition of the bark's future wreck, and to all appearances the isles did belong to a completely phantom world. Despite all the details given in the *Federation*'s logbook no explanation was found for their appearance on the ship's course. It was generally assumed that the affair must have been some sort of collective illusion, until a survey mission off the Chinese coast made a startling discovery which could hold the key to the mystery.

They discovered that during the rainy season flood waters detached masses of soil from riverbanks, some of them the size of small islands. These floating islets of mud and clay, forming compact masses often with plants and bushes still growing on them, were known to drift out to sea at the mercy of winds and currents. It could have been two of these that terrified the *Federation*'s crew.

The story of this bark's adventure has been put first in this book because it is typical of the kind of island mysteries we are dealing with. There are islands scattered over the oceans of the world and many of them have strange tales attached to them, either through their very existence, or as the scenes of unexplained events, or simply because of some mysterious attraction, persisting over the centuries. There are phantom islands that have appeared for a day and never been seen again; there are isles of violence, stained with untold crimes; there are real mirages that have been clearly visible in full sunlight; and there are islands such as those that claimed Stevenson, Gauguin, Alain Gerbault, and held them to the end of their lives. There are treasure islands, isles of paradise, isles of purgatory or salvation, where shipwrecked sailors have waited, often in vain, for rescue.

It is no mere chance that after two and a half centuries *Robinson Crusoe* is still one of the world's most widely read stories. Islands draw us as ships do, and like them they are the symbols of all man's subconscious longing for happiness, love, freedom from responsibility and the chance of a fresh start, all the motives that drive him to outlandish adventures.

Islands are the password opening a door of escape into the unknown, and this explains why the voyage we are undertaking is one into the realms of mystery.

2

Alone Against the Isle

THE *Boston Gazette* for July 18, 1811, carried a strange paragraph on its fourth page, so strange indeed that the paper's editor received numerous protests and canceled subscriptions from readers who, having previously believed the *Boston Gazette* to be a sober and responsible newspaper, now protested that they had lost all confidence in it.

The fuss resulted from a simple announcement by an American, Jonathan Lambert, a native of Salem, Massachusetts, that he intended taking absolute possession of the island of Tristan da Cunha for himself and his heirs forever. Lambert went on to say that he was adopting the title of Emperor, his realm would thenceforth be known as the Isle of Rest, and his flag would be five whole and four half diamonds in red and blue on a green ground.

The Americans viewed the new Emperor's accession with considerable suspicion, regarding it as impossible in the nineteenth century for a private individual, unheard of until that moment, to annex an island, with no other right than "occupation of land of which no other nation had ever formally taken possession."

But the skeptics were wrong, for on the very day the announcement appeared Jonathan Lambert raised his flag over Tristan da Cunha, a remote and curious island which, even in our own day, remains the most isolated in the world.

Isolated in the South Atlantic roughly between Cape Horn and the Cape of Good Hope and some 1,500 miles from St. Helena, its highest point rises 8,500 feet above the southern swell. There is scarcely any level ground; nearly everywhere outcrops of black volcanic rock overhang the sparse strips of grassland and narrow, wave-lashed beaches.

It was on one of these that, three months earlier, Lambert and a few companions had struggled ashore with a few chests which they stowed in the shelter of the rocks amid the thundering surf and the incessant cries of myriads of gulls, petrels and cormorants.

Who was Lambert? No one ever really knew. It was said he was a ship's captain and, assuming the vessel was a private ship, there may well be some truth in this. Lambert's motive in establishing himself on the island could have been to escape the attentions of the Navy and secure his booty.

Tristan da Cunha was first discovered in 1505 by the Portuguese navigator who gave it his name and who was satisfied to chart its position without attempting a landing. Later it was rediscovered by the Dutch, who did not consider the island of any interest. The Frenchmen Etcheverry, in 1767, Dupetit-Thouars, in 1793, and Bory de St. Vincent in 1801, each noticed the lonely island in his turn, and Dupetit-Thouars in particular was convinced of the possibilities of colonization. Jonathan Lambert shared his opinion and envisaged a peaceful life devoted to hunting sea lions, growing cereals and raising pigs and goats.

But he made a mistake in yielding to the desire to proclaim his sovereignty for, on March 5, 1813, HMS *Semiramis*, battered by a strong westerly gale, fought her way to Tristan da Cunha with its perpetual crown of clouds. Captain Richardson was under orders to remind Lambert that the island was a British possession.

The officer was met by a man dressed in rags.

"Are you Jonathan Lambert?" asked Richardson.

"No. My name is Thomas Corrie."

"Where are Lambert and his friends?"

"They disappeared one night when there was a storm."

Richardson suspected a trick, but the neglected crops and ruined village proved Corrie was telling the truth, he really was alone. All Corrie would say about the "Emperor's" disappearance was that Lambert had set off on a fishing expedition one afternoon and had not returned. A terrible storm had raged during the night and Lambert was never seen again.

Corrie refused to leave the island and Richardson did not urge him. He was sure there was some private reason for Corrie's determination to remain on Tristan but had no time to waste on solving the problem. He ran up the British flag on the beach and the *Semiramis* weighed anchor, leaving behind her at the foot of the towering black cliffs the scarecrow figure of Corrie, standing rigidly beside the pole where the flag flapped in the icy southeasterly.

Some time later a whaler dropped anchor for a few hours off the island. Corrie went on board and accepted some supplies, but once again refused repatriation.

"But there is one thing I should like to ask," he told the captain.

"What is it?"

"I should like a wife to share my life."

The captain made a vague promise to let the Governor of the Cape know of the request, and for two years Thomas Corrie waited for his helpmate. At last on August 14, 1816, an English corvette appeared but, instead of the woman he hoped for, the bewildered Corrie saw armed soldiers coming ashore. Hudson Lowe, the Governor of St. Helena, had decided to occupy Tristan in case it should provide a base for future Bonapartist attempts to liberate the Emperor.

For a few days Corrie was shattered and made no attempt to mix with those he considered intruders, but then, slowly, he began coming to the soldiers and asking them for spirits.

"Not without money," the corporal told him.

Corrie said nothing and came back two hours later to ask for a glass of gin.

"Have you any money?" asked the corporal.

Corrie held out a gold piece. The corporal bit the coin to see if it was good, then stared at it in amazement. It bore the head of Philip II of Spain.

It seemed fairly clear that Corrie had stumbled on a pirate's hoard but he would never reveal its whereabouts, although he referred to a chest landed by the "Emperor" Lambert, who had vanished so mysteriously one night, and later admitted that the chest was buried between two waterfalls at "Little Beach."

Nothing more was ever found out, for Corrie died soon afterward and all searches were unsuccessful. There is still treasure to be found on Tristan da Cunha.

But it was not the treasure that drew the Stoltenhoff brothers to the lonely island where they were to live through such strange experiences.

"A fortune . . . a fortune to be picked up for the asking. . . ."

Frederick Stoltenhoff listened to his brother's voice and gazed out of the window at the peaceful rooftops of Aix-la-Chapelle, golden in the early spring sunshine. On finishing his military service he had been on the point of resuming, without much enthusiasm, his uneventful life as a clerk in a commercial firm when his brother Gustav casually offered him a fortune, if not altogether for the asking, on a lonely island in the South Atlantic.

"In two years we can make enough to live in comfort for the rest of our lives," persisted Gustav.

"But where is this island?"

"Fifteen hundred miles south of St. Helena."

"What is it called?"

"Tristan da Cunha."

Gustav talked on. He had signed on as a seaman in an English bark which had caught fire in the region of Tristan da Cunha. The crew had taken refuge on the island and

Gustav and his companions would never forget that black cone thrusting out of the ocean. Huddled in their boat they had watched the weird shape, rising before them like a guardian monster of the deep, and they had been terrified of natives they believed would be as wild as their home.

They had quickly been reassured. The inhabitants treated them kindly and offered them food, and when the shipwrecked sailors were put aboard a passing vessel three weeks later they retained the happiest memories of Tristan da Cunha. Gustav Stoltenhoff in particular had sailed back to Europe with his mind full of the vast numbers of seals whose black flocks covered the island's rocky shores.

"Do you know sealskins and seal oil are very valuable and you could make your fortune out of them?" Stoltenhoff had asked the islanders.

"Make our fortunes? What for?" they answered him.

They were still totally ignorant of money. Gustav shrugged his shoulders and calculated the profit to be made from the seals. He made up his mind to return to Tristan da Cunha.

Back in Germany he told his brother what he intended and suggested a partnership, but Frederick hesitated. A fortune there might be, but to gain possession of it there were the dangers of the stormy, unknown island in uncharted seas to be faced and a hard life, full of danger and difficulty, to be endured. But for a young man the risk seemed no worse than committing himself to a quiet humdrum existence such as awaited him in his native town.

Gradually Frederick found himself drawn to the magic of the island and felt the pull of the solitary land in the midst of the sea, like a world in formation, rich in promises and possibilities.

"Well, when will you decide?" asked Gustav.

Frederick stood up and smiled. He had heard the call of the islands.

"A fortnight from now and you'll be in Tristan."

The captain of the whaler the Stoltenhoff brothers boarded in August 1871 listened to their proposals doubtfully at first, but gradually the young men's spirit impressed him and as they approached their destination he began loading them with advice. During their call at St. Helena he supervised their purchases: a sailing dinghy, spades, tools, provisions.

"I think you'll have everything you need," said the captain. "I'll give you some vegetable seeds as well. Don't worry, you aren't going to die of starvation. There's only one thing worries me a bit and that's how the Tristanites will take to you."

"The Tristanites?"

"That's what the inhabitants are called."

"Why," asked Gustav, "don't you think they'll be pleased to see us?"

The captain did not answer.

Gustav persisted. "After my ship was wrecked they were all right, kindness itself in fact."

"Yes, because you were shipwrecked and they knew you wouldn't be staying long."

"We don't intend to spend the rest of our lives on Tristan."

"They may believe you but, believe me, that doesn't

make things any easier. I've stayed there four or five times, and the Tristanites were perfectly friendly and helpful; but when two of my men talked of making their home on the island the people turned cold to the point of hostility. What can you expect? They're so isolated they're bound to be a bit uncouth."

Gustav's face was creased with thought.

"It doesn't really make much difference to us, because we're well provided for and need no one. We were thinking of Tristan rather as a desert island."

"Why don't you settle on a real desert island right away?" asked the captain. "Another island where there are plenty of seals."

"Do you know one?"

"Yes, only fourteen or fifteen miles from Tristan. Inaccessible Island. It looks pretty forbidding but don't let that put you off; the interior is wooded and there is fertile soil. Besides, the climate is milder than Tristan and I can tell you whaling crews have camped there comfortably for several weeks at a time."

The American whaler sighted Tristan da Cunha on November 26th, and the following day hove to off the west coast of Inaccessible Island.

The Stoltenhoff brothers looked at the sheer cliffs, some of them well over 1,000 feet high, a fearsome battlement with the foaming surf boiling at their feet. Sea birds screamed in the lowering sky. To their right a beach of black stones went steeply down to the sea, hemmed in by bracken and twisted bushes.

Every man on board stood in awe-struck silence staring at the island, which rose like some monstrous, stern-faced idol erected to placate the fierce spirits of the sea. In the stillness they could hear the continuous angry roar of waves pounding on the rocks. Covertly watching the two Germans, the seamen saw their faces were grave.

"There's your desert island," said the captain with forced heartiness. "It's all yours and no one will come and interfere with your work."

He shouted an order and provisions were stowed in the boat. There were 200 pounds of flour, the same of rice, 100 pounds of biscuit, 20 pounds of coffee, 10 pounds of tea, 30 pounds of sugar, and some wine and spirits. Then, three dogs, the tools, arms and ammunition were unloaded.

"You haven't forgotten my library?" asked Gustav.

They showed him a little case of books; travels, Schiller's poems, Shakespeare.

"I don't think we've forgotten anything," he repeated. "Thank you all."

The two brothers shook hands with the crew and listened to the captain's parting advice: "Take good care of your boat. I'm sure the Tristanites will come to your help if you need them. Light a fire, they can see that when the weather is fine. May God protect you."

Half an hour later as the whaler was drawing away from the shore one of the sailors gave a cry. The moving background of clouds made it seem as though the beetling cliffs were on the point of falling and crushing the still figures of the two Germans who stood as if turned to stone at their feet.

Gustav and Frederick were afraid, weighed down and tormented by a fear whose very vagueness only made it worse. The whaler's sails dipped below the horizon and they were alone; yet not alone, for the island seemed to be peopled with invisible presences. Even the three dogs sniffed suspiciously at the dark rocks and scrub as if they could smell strange tracks, and from time to time one of them would stop and give a hoarse bark that echoed eerily in the silence disturbed only by the myriad noises of wind and sea.

The two men turned. Behind them lay the unknown is-island, wrapped in dark clouds and haunted by petrels and cormorants, an island that somehow, however slowly, they had to conquer. Before them lay the ocean which they had no hope of crossing in their small dinghy.

Without speaking Gustav moved across to one of the cases heaped on the rocks and began dragging it into the shelter of a cave. The familiar noises of planks clattering on the stones, breaking wood and hammering cleared the gloom that had engulfed the two brothers, and prevented their brooding on the hard facts of their isolation. But a few hours later as night fell they felt again all the weight of depression.

Lying in their tent they thought again of their hazardous venture, cast away on a desert island whose very stones seemed to reject them. All around them were the noises of the night. Gusts of wind shook the tent until its canvas cracked like gunfire and the gale made a thousand more disturbing and meaningless sounds as it tore at the sharp rocks.

Neither Frederick nor Gustav slept. They lay with their eyes open peering anxiously into the darkness as if trying to discern what lay before them.

With daylight their courage returned and the brothers began building a hut and laying out a vegetable garden. They ventured a little way into the interior and found the lake the captain had mentioned. It was the beginning of the southern summer and the weather was mild and dry. By the end of a week their lives had fallen into a sort of pattern and they were ready to begin hunting their first seals, when one morning they thought they could hear voices coming from the sea.

"Birds, I expect," Gustav said.

They started with surprise as they saw a whaling boat emerge from behind the group of rocks which had been hiding it and head toward the beach.

Gustav and Frederick stared at the boat full of men as it rose and fell with the heaving of the swell, wondering whether it held a potential danger. It mght be another seal-hunting expedition intending to settle on the island for several weeks, or even months, to make war on the seals with methods more efficient and up-to-date than their own.

When the new arrivals' faces could be distinguished they showed no surprise at the sight of the two Germans and the men simply raised their arms in greeting. The Stoltenhoffs returned the salute mechanically as the whaler's prow grated on the shingle.

"Have you been shipwrecked?" inquired one of the newcomers, a man of about forty with a slight smile on his weather-beaten face.

Gustav answered him. "No, my brother and I are camping here to hunt seals."

"What ship are you from?"

"None. We are alone."

29

"Alone?"

The man turned to his companions and he was no longer smiling. Evidently here was something he did not understand although he did not like to ask for an explanation. He simply said, "We too have come to hunt seals."

"Are you from Europe?" Gustav asked him.

"No. We live on Tristan da Cunha."

In 1871 Tristan da Cunha was no longer the desert island it had been in Jonathan Lambert's time. The population had slowly begun to increase ever since three English soldiers had asked to stay there with their families after the recall of the garrison in 1816. They had been joined by a handful of sailors, castaways or deserters; in particular a Dutchman, Peter William Green, who was for many years king of the island.

Some more women had come to the island at the request of the Governor of the Cape in 1825, and by 1871 the population had swelled to a hundred and fifty. Believing their island could not support a greater number, the Tristanites strongly opposed any further attempts at colonization, and this was the reason for their anxiety at the sight of the brothers.

"Do you intend to stay here long?" asked their spokesman.

"That depends on the hunting."

Gustav remembered the captain's warning and his reply was cautious, but the attitude of the Tristanites remained reserved, although not threatening. They paid a visit to the camp and criticized the site, saying that the brothers would do better to settle in the north of the island. To their objection that the north face was inaccessible, the Tristanites said that it had to be reached by boat and showed them a route avoiding surface rocks and dangerous pools. They also showed the brothers how to build a firm house, sheltered from the rockfalls that were a common occurrence on stormy days when huge masses of rock were liable to break away from the cliff face.

They did not invite the Germans to share their hunting, and in the event did not have any luck, departing after ten days having failed to capture a single animal.

"You noticed they didn't ask us to come over to Tristan?" said Frederick when their visitors had gone.

"The main thing is they left us alone to work," replied Gustav.

They did work very well and in less than a fortnight had killed and salted nineteen seals, although they did not succeed in extracting the oil.

When not fishing the brothers made improvements to their house and dug the garden. They became bolder in their explorations of the island and made a startling discovery.

There was a high plateau rising some hundreds of feet above sea level and the Tristanites had asked whether they had climbed this. But when the brothers said no and asked them why, they had made no answer and had begun talking of other things. The Germans thought nothing of their silence at the time but, considering it afterward, they became curious and finally made up their minds to explore the plateau and find out its secret.

At first sight the climb looked impossible. For the first hundred and fifty feet or so it was simply a matter of scrambling up the rocks, but beyond that the cliff face was a mass of long, tangled grass.

Yet if the Tristanites had spoken of the plateau they must have been up there, and Gustav and Frederick asked themselves how they could have done it. It was Gustav who found the answer. The clumps of grass that appeared to be an obstacle were in fact a help, since they were sufficiently firmly rooted for a man to grab and support his weight on it. Exploring the ground on his attempt, Gustav marked a sort of path and bound some of the tussocks into bunches at regular intervals to make them easier to grasp. Then he was ready.

Frederick watched anxiously from the shore as his brother's figure moved slowly up the cliff face. Hanging between the boiling surf and the torn clouds Gustav would pause, feel his way back a few yards, then go on again, sometimes disappearing in the long grass, and at these moments Frederick would feel the terror of being left quite alone on the island.

The climb took several hours but at last Gustav hauled himself upright on the plateau and waved triumphantly at his brother. Then he disappeared and once more Frederick felt the panic fear of loneliness. He had never been in favor of the climb, which he considered useless, and now he stared hopelessly after his brother. Long minutes passed but there was no sign of Gustav. Frederick shouted, and as he listened to the derisive echoes of his voice borne away on the wind fear gripped him. For an instant above the immense cliff, half hidden in mist, with its pelt of moving grass that made it seem like some monstrous creature breathing, he caught a glimpse of a long head topped by a pair of horns.

The vision lasted no more than a second, but it set Frederick shivering and sweating with sheer terror. What weird inhabitants haunted the plateau, he wondered, what monstrous beings, survivors of a vanished race, had retreated there to die out slowly on this rocky peak like shipwrecked sailors clutching the spars of their foundering vessel?

Frederick stared upward with dilated eyes and gave one strangled shriek, hoarse with despair, a cry for help that was swallowed up in the muffled clamor of wind and sea.

At that instant the head appeared a second time, showing so clearly that Frederick could no longer hope he had been imagining it. The thing grinned at him over the abyss, a hairy head surmounted by an unmistakable pair of horns.

Unreasoning panic swept over Frederick and he began running toward the plateau, as though hypnotized by the peril awaiting him. He clutched desperately at handfuls of grass, feeling fragments of rock shift under his feet and measuring his advance up the face of the cliff by the time they took to clatter onto the beach below. Occasionally he cast a fearful glance upward, expecting to see again the frightful head, but nothing moved.

Frederick climbed on, his mind a blank, no longer even sure what was driving him up toward the plateau. Suddenly he turned and began making his way downward. His brother had appeared on the cliff top and was waving toward the beach. A few hours later Gustav had rejoined him on the shore.

"Well?" asked Frederick.

33

"It was all right."

"You can't think how scared I was. It's ridiculous but I thought I saw fabulous monsters moving about on the edge of the plateau."

Gustav burst out laughing.

"You weren't imagining them. They are our best piece of luck yet."

"What do you mean?"

"Do you know what I found up there?"

"How can I know?" said his brother irritably.

"Pigs and goats."

"Impossible!"

"That's what I thought. But it's true."

"Who could have brought them there?"

"It's a mystery, but it's fact. I counted twenty-three goats and eighteen pigs."

"So what I saw . . ."

"Was a goat. And you were so scared you didn't recognize it."

Always supposing they could reach the plateau easily, which at the present was far from the case, the miraculous livestock represented food for months.

"There must be some easier way to reach the plateau," said Gustav.

The brothers hunted furiously, exploring every bay and creek in their boat and carefully noting the beginnings of anything that looked like a track, until at last they found what they sought. In the west corner of the island a steep path wound right up to the summit. They climbed it and soon Frederick too was standing on the plateau, which consisted of a sort of grass-covered prairie, sheltered to the north by a pile of rocks, where the flocks were grazing.

Only one thing worried them. It was impossible to get to the plateau except from the west, which was the side of the island opposite their camp, and then only when the sea was calm. This was about once a week during fine weather, but in the winter there was the risk that they would be completely cut off from the plateau at the time when, with fishing bad and perhaps impossible, their need of fresh meat was greatest.

They returned to their camp intending to try to improve the route Gustav had used with such difficulty in his first climb, but they had not cleared more than a few yards before it became obvious they could not go much farther. They could not stand sufficiently upright on the almost vertical slope to handle pick and shovel.

"There's no point in exhausting ourselves for nothing," said Gustav.

"Giving up?"

"With the pick, yes. But there is another way."

"How?" asked Frederick.

"Fire. If we go carefully we can clear a path."

The trickiest part of the operation would be to keep the path narrow, leaving tussocks of grass at the edge, which were necessary if they were to climb at all. They chose a day when the weather was calm with just enough southerly wind to drive the flames toward the summit, Gustav and Frederick stood on either side of the track to prevent the flames from spreading and at first things went very well, although more slowly than they had hoped. But after one or two attempts the wind dropped and the flames died out.

"We'll carry on all the same," said Gustav.

They lit the fire once more and the path had grown another few yards when a sudden gust of wind sprang up and fanned the dwindling blaze. The flames leaped higher and spread to left and right, making a suffocating cloud of smoke, until within moments several square yards were blazing. At first the Germans attempted to fight the fire but it was a losing battle. The flames rolled headlong toward the summit leaving only scorched and blackened rock in their wake.

That night Gustav and Frederick crouched in their hut and watched the burning cliff and saw wisps of smoke still rising to mingle with the morning mist. Daylight revealed the full extent of the catastrophe.

A catastrophe it was. Over an area of several hundred feet the tufts of grass that afforded a handhold had completely vanished. The cliff was all one smooth, black expanse, putting the plateau with its stock of fresh meat beyond their reach. The loss was the more disastrous, for the winter was beginning and huge waves made the sea all but impassable to their boat.

"All the same we'll have to try sailing," decided Gustav. "We'll bring back as many pigs and goats as we can carry."

They made for the shallow creek where they had moored their boat and found to their horror that the boat was gone.

"But we moored her fast," groaned Frederick.

They had not far to look for an answer to the mystery. The whaler was still where they had left her but lying at the bottom of the water. She had been battered against the rocks by the surf and had sunk. They managed to haul the wreck onto dry land, only to find that her whole stern had been stove in and was beyond repair. They attempted to saw off the broken timbers, shortening the boat by six feet or more, but although she floated again she had become clumsy and unmanageable. From then on their expeditions to the west coast became dangerous until, in June, they ceased altogether, when the boat was caught in a storm and totally wrecked.

Now the winter seas battered Inaccessible Island without a break and the island was the center of a boiling mass of green spray. The Stoltenhoff brothers lived in a state of continual fear. Making an inventory of their remaining stores, they found they had left only enough potatoes and salt fish to last them a month, or six weeks with careful rationing.

Now and then their eyes were raised to the plateau where the pigs and goats that would feed them through the winter months were grazing peacefully. Up there lay salvation, but a salvation beyond their reach. They were cut off from hope by the black wall of the cliff down which the rain streamed, only dried here and there by the raging wind.

"The west side . . ." wondered Gustav.

If they could only get to the west side, the way to the plateau was easy. The brothers stared at the wreckage of their boat that cut them off completely. They had not enough wood to build another, certainly not one strong enough to withstand the battering waves that pounded unceasingly on the shore, drenching their camp in a continuous mist of spray.

The sea put a stop to all activity and the brothers felt

that the ocean was no more their enemy than the desolate land to which they had rashly committed themselves. They were prisoners of the island and its lowering mists and clouds, where sun shone only in infrequent short bursts.

One morning in March Gustav was making yet another hopeless attempt to fashion a canoe from the remains of their whaler when he saw his brother rush hastily into the hut and emerge carrying his gun. He fired several shots, then began hurriedly collecting sticks to make a fire. A thick smoke started to rise over the shore but, although Gustav scanned the horizon, it remained empty as far as the eye could see. He shouted to Frederick, who pointed to the north.

He must be seeing things, thought Gustav.

He himself had more than once believed he had sighted a ship out there, but the shape had always dissolved into nothing, or a dark cloud twisted by the wind to look like a ship.

But Frederick seemed perfectly satisfied with his vision, so Gustav too began to hope. He peered through the telescope into the gloom and gave a cry as a ship appeared through the mist. She was close-reefed and was tacking toward the island. It seemed as if she had seen the Germans' signals but was proceeding cautiously, as though her captain knew the inadequacy of charts in these latitudes and was taking no chances.

The two brothers watched the ship. They would be able to exchange their sealskins for fresh victuals, clothes, liquor, tobacco, perhaps even a boat. They had mental visions of a boat to take them to the western shore and saw themselves returning to camp laden with pigs and goats, able to eat their fill. They could already smell the roast meat.

The ship was still in sight and they assumed her captain was waiting for a break in the surf before trying to heave to, but there was no sign of approaching calm. Gusts of wind whitened the surface of the water and battered against the island's rocky walls with such strength that it seemed to be wearing away the very face of the cliff.

Frederick feverishly tended his fire, from time to time firing a few shots into the growling storm, and it may have been this that interested the captain of the strange bark which still hovered offshore.

"It's not possible," groaned Frederick. "They haven't seen us."

But after covering the length of the beach from about half a mile out the ship was finally turning to the shore.

"They must have seen us," said Gustav. "Otherwise they would have kept much farther offshore."

"But they're going away."

"No vessel could make a landfall through this surf. They'll be looking for a more sheltered piece of coast."

"But if they come ashore anywhere else they won't be able to reach us."

The two brothers stared after the ship as long as she could be seen but within half an hour she had been hidden by a jutting headland.

"She'll come back. When her captain finds he can't reach us by land he'll have another try off the beach."

Gustav's voice lacked conviction. That the captain would make a circuit of the island was likely but the bad weather might well make him feel he had no right to risk his ship and the lives of his men for the sake of any poor wretches who might be alive on that miserable strip of land.

Night fell quickly. Despite the presence of a ship close at hand, the Stoltenhoffs had never felt more desolate and alone. All night long they fired shots and tended the fire, a pathetic flicker of light in the high wind, and as dawn came they stared hopefully at the horizon. Only the empty sea emerged from the darkness.

The Stoltenhoffs waited all day but by evening they had lost hope. The gale still raged over the deserted waters.

In April Gustav and Frederick caught no more than a dozen fish and these were their only fresh food. They lived on, weak and emaciated, with nothing to occupy their time beyond waiting for a calm, as though it would miraculously bring the ship back to them; but the island was still buffeted by storms.

To conserve their strength they lay in their hut for hours at a time listening to the wind battering on the walls and dreaming of impossible festivities.

In this way June and July passed. The brothers no longer ate a solid meal more than once every two or three days. The rest of the time they swallowed an insipid broth made of herbs which appeased their hunger but gave them little nourishment. Sometimes they would crawl out of the hut, the bones sticking through their skin, to hunt for game, but with the exception of a few sea birds that flew too high to be caught, every living creature seemed to have deserted the island.

By August they no longer hoped for anything. They simply existed, doing nothing, waiting for nothing, eating anything they could find.

One night as they lay trying to sleep they heard, through the howling gale that had formed a perpetual background to their lives for many months, a steady crunching on the pebbly beach. They held their breath but it was not a dream. The crunching grew louder until it sounded like the footsteps of an invading army.

The brothers wondered what could be the reason for the strange noise. They thought at first of pebbles sucked by the waves, but the sound continued. It was definitely the sound of cautious footsteps. Could it be the Tristanites come to dispossess the intruders, or the crew of a whaling or seal-hunting vessel, or perhaps even the survivors of a shipwreck? The brothers waited, staring into the darkness as if paralyzed by the mysterious footsteps, unable to open their cabin door though they knew if people had really landed on the island their deliverance might be at hand.

They had so often imagined the joys of rescue, of speaking and eating again as human beings, but now they were unable to make a move toward the invisible presences that surrounded them.

"What do you think it is?" asked Frederick at last. Gustav seized his gun and a lantern.

"Better go and see," he said.

He went out, followed by his brother, and at once they were swallowed up in the howling night, the breath knocked out of them by the icy blast that pierced their emaciated bodies.

Gradually their eyes cleared and they were able to make

out the harsh landscape that had grown familiar to them.
"I can't see anyone," muttered Gustav.

The lantern's feeble yellow light carved a circle a few
feet in diameter out of the blackness and in it they moved
hesitantly toward the shore.

"How did they manage to land?" gasped Frederick.

The two brothers seemed to be living in a dream and
their reactions were no longer those of sane men. Fear took
hold of them and dried their mouths and turned their knees
to water. Twice they faltered and almost yielded to the
panic that urged them to run and hide, cowering in their
hut like animals from an imaginary danger; but they recovered and went on, led by the wavering lantern light.

The strangers never moved. Their silhouettes were
thrown against the waves breaking on the shore like a
screen and seemed oddly small, possibly because they were
standing low down on the beach which here sloped
steeply into the sea.

Someone gave a feeble shout. It was Gustav, but he
heard no reply except the thunder of the waves on the
shore and the mysterious footsteps. Gustav shouted again,
waving his lantern, and when there was still no reply he
fired a shot in the air.

The crunching sounds below them increased as the
strangers scattered in all directions.

"We're friends," called Frederick.

Gustav said nothing and began walking purposefully toward the sea. Frederick watched his figure melt into the
night amid the tearing, crashing surf, the howling wind
and the strange footsteps.

Gustav walked on grimly. He had made up his mind to

end their uncertainty and he waited for the figures to rise into the light of his lantern. The crunching began again, closer this time and more distinct.

One question was bothering Gustav above all others. Why were the men so small? Had chance brought his brother and himself to an island inhabited by some legendary dwarfs or pygmies of the sea whose existence had hitherto been unsuspected? Such an idea seemed quite natural to him, for privation, suffering and sheer physical weakness all sharpened his imagination and made him unusually susceptible to fantasies and hallucinations. He became convinced he was about to fight against an army of dwarfs. Certainly he was going to fight something, because if the new arrivals were friendly why were they keeping so quiet? Had they been coming to save them, he reasoned, they would have made themselves known long before.

Gustav waited with his finger on the trigger for the lamplight to shine full on his enemies before he fired. The footsteps came nearer and nearer until he could control himself no longer and fired at random into the darkness in front of him.

For a moment there was silence, a complete stillness in which even the sound of the sea seemed muffled, then the footsteps began again, surrounding Gustav and hemming him in until at last he could see a dozen of the island's invaders in the lamplight.

After one moment of paralyzing astonishment Gustav broke into hysterical laughter. When he could speak once more he shouted to his brother.

"Hey, Frederick! Come and see. Come on, there's nothing to be afraid of!"

The brothers' terror was replaced by delight, for their sufferings were at an end, at least for a few months. In a matter of a few hours the island had become filled with a colony of penguins, and it was their footsteps on the beach and their indistinct figures that the brothers had seen and heard in the night.

By the middle of September the brothers were as strong and active as ever. They were able to eat their fill, for the silly, trusting penguins were easily killed with a blow and the island's rocky ledges were crammed with their eggs.

One morning when a ship dropped anchor off the island her captain hailed them and asked if they wanted a passage back to Europe.

"Three weeks ago we should have said yes," answered the brothers. "We were almost dead with hunger."

"And now?"

"Now we've made up our minds to stay for at least another fishing season."

The captain could not spare them the boat they asked for, but he did give them a supply of fresh food. The Germans were filled with renewed confidence, as though they had undergone the tests the island imposed on them and felt in future it would leave them in peace. They knew now the trials that would face them and had learned how to struggle and survive.

As the southern summer drew on they saw several sails on the inhospitable sea, and one day in October they heard voices and footsteps on the beach in the early morning. It was the crew of a whaler, the *Themis*, whose sails could be seen flapping idly in the morning air. Some Tristanites came ashore from her, and their attitude was much less friendly than on their previous visit. They were not after seals and the brothers suspected their object was the reserve of pigs and goats on the plateau.

The Tristanites rounded the western headland in a small boat and returned in the evening bearing bloodstained sacks which they loaded aboard the *Themis*. They exchanged few words with the brothers, who read in their set faces and unfriendly stares the knowledge that they had tried to avail themselves of the livestock. The whaler sailed the next day and the brothers were again left to themselves.

Gustav and Frederick were by now restored to perfect health and only one thing troubled them. They had not managed to persuade the *Themis'* captain to leave them a boat.

"I've already lost one in a squall," he explained.

The Tristanites for their part answered evasively that boats were hard to come by but they did promise to pass on the request to the next vessel that put in at Tristan da Cunha.

But the brothers were determined not to endure again the long agony of weakness and delirium in their hut throughout the winter months.

"Whatever happens we must reach the plateau," said Gustav firmly.

"But how? You know as well as I do it's impossible unless we have a boat."

"We'll do without a boat. We'll swim around to the other side. It's the only way."

They waited for a calm day, then wrapped blankets,

guns, clothes, powder, matches and provisions in two sacks.

"It's like going on holiday," said Frederick with a smile. A grim holiday, with death perhaps at the end.

They plunged into the sea. Despite the temptation to keep close to the shore for safety in case of cramp, they preferred to swim farther out where the current was less strong and they could make better progress. Avoiding the surface rocks with their clouds of spray and hovering sea birds, the swimmers rounded the western headland.

"Shall we go in?" gasped Frederick.

"No," answered Gustav. "Hang on for another half mile and we'll get the benefit of the crosscurrent that will take us in easily."

But now they began to find themselves caught in the ground swell and the island sometimes disappeared from sight altogether as they slid into the trough of a wave. Surrounded by the glassy ramparts of water, the brothers felt a peculiar sense of fear, a total desolation that was like being irrevocably cut off from life. Then slowly the high black cliffs began to draw nearer and an hour later they dragged themselves wearily onto the western shore.

The next day they climbed to the plateau, that unattainable paradise that had filled their dreams all winter. They were already thinking of the cabin they intended to build between the two great piles of rock that served as a barrier against the wind. They would live incomparably better there than on their strip of seashore, and the pigs and goats would provide a reserve of meat ready to hand.

For a few hours the brothers indulged their imagination, but they already knew how far the dream was from reality. While it would undoubtedly be more comfortable to live on the plateau than close to the shore, it would also mean an end to the very reason for their presence on the island. Seal hunting would be impossible. Moreover on the plateau they would run the risk of even greater isolation in not being able to take advantage of a ship if one appeared.

Gustav thought hard. It was equally unthinkable to give up their fishing or the resources offered by the plateau.

"There might be one way," he said at last. "One of us could stay here and the other go down."

"Separate?"

"It may be the only way to survive. I could hunt seals and look after the garden and you could take care of the animals and kill one every so often."

"How could I send you the meat?"

"Throw it down to me from the top of the cliff. You can hardly miss."

Frederick had suffered more than his brother from the hardships of their first year on the island and he became more restless and uneasy as the moment of separation approached. Gustav reassured him by insisting their life would be much more bearable and neither would die of starvation. Frederick finally allowed himself to be persuaded and, after staying two days on the plateau, his brother left him, taking with him three pigs in a wooden cage.

The descent was a comparatively easy one and it was not this that made Frederick uneasy, but the long swim which Gustav would have to accomplish on his own, dragging with him the cage containing the pigs. He waited anxiously, scanning the sea and leaning over to the beach to

47

watch for his brother's approach. Night came on, turning the waves to a gray mass and blurring the shape of the island, but there was no sign of Gustav.

Frederick was seized with sudden panic. He saw himself alone on the island without a boat to take him as far as Tristan da Cunha, a helpless castaway. The beach below him was still deserted.

Occasionally Frederick would make out a dark speck on the ocean, but it always turned out to be only floating driftwood or seaweed or the tip of a protruding rock and not the swimmer he had hoped. He shouted hopelessly from time to time, knowing quite well his brother could not hear him. The first stars came out and there was still no sign of life from Gustav.

I'll go down myself as soon as it's light, thought Frederick, lying in his hut unable to sleep, a prey to all sorts of fears. He clutched at faint hopes. His brother must have stopped to rest on a rock, tired of dragging the pigs' cage. He had great endurance and was used to swimming long distances, and moreover the sea was very calm. He knew the currents and could hardly have been trapped by them.

At about one in the morning Frederick sat up. He had not seen or heard anything but he had smelled something, the smell of smoke from a wood fire rising into the air.

He got up and, taking a lantern, moved cautiously to the cliff edge. The wind had fallen, there was a clear sky and, a rare enough thing, Inaccessible Island was in deep silence. Frederick leaned toward the beach, invisible in the darkness, and yelled his brother's name.

Near the camp at his feet a fire glowed redly and the damp wood gave off a thick smoke that rose to the plateau.

It could only have been lighted by Gustav. Gustav was safe.

Frederick stared at the distant spark for a long time until at last it went out.

"How many seals have you got today?"

The voice echoed from the rocky wall, multiplying itself in endless reverberations and losing the words in the nooks and crannies of the cliff so that Gustav on the beach below could not make out what his brother was trying to say. A new life had begun for the two Germans and its greatest trial was their mutual loneliness.

Whenever the wind dropped and the sea ceased its loud battering on the island's shore, the brothers could sustain this illusion of conversation which was their only link. Gustav grew potatoes, fished, melted down the pork fat which Frederick threw down to him wrapped in a bag of hide, and succeeded in harpooning one or two seals on the beach. They communicated three times a day by signs and this habit kept their morale reasonably high.

Gustav was surprised one morning in late April when his brother did not appear as usual. This was particularly strange because the weather was very calm and they could have conversed quite easily, and it was unlike Frederick to lose such an opportunity. When at midday he again saw no sign of Frederick, Gustav began to be anxious. His brother was not so busily occupied on the plateau that he would forget to show himself; he must be ill or have met with an accident.

I can't just stay here doing nothing, Gustav told himself. Tomorrow I'll climb up to the plateau.

That afternoon he had no heart for work but spent the time preparing for the next day's expedition, often turning to look up at the plateau. But no one appeared.

Gustav's anxiety increased. If his brother were ill or hurt there could be no question of bringing him down to the camp, yet if they were to take advantage of any passing ship this would be the best place for him. It was still possible to call on the Tristanites but, even if they were to see his signals, Gustav was by no means confident they would come to his help.

At this point his reflections were interrupted by the dogs who were barking loudly at something floating in the sea a hundred yards or so from shore.

Flotsam, he thought.

Any pieces of wreckage were a godsend to the brothers. Wood was very scarce on the islands. There was even a legend that on Tristan da Cunha the girls prayed God to "send them a good shipwreck" so that they could get married, since wood for their hearths was one of the young couples' chief necessities.

Gustav decided to swim out and fetch the strange object. Reaching it quite easily, he dragged it back to the beach. It was a sort of clumsily made cage containing a pig. The pig had been drowned.

Gustav flung himself down on the wet stones. He knew that only Frederick could have made the cage and his mind easily filled in the remainder of the tragedy. Taking advantage of the fine weather, Frederick must have tried to get to the camp and bring Gustav the animal, but he had probably been seized by cramp and had let go the cage, which had floated away. As for Frederick himself . . .

Gustav plunged back into the sea determined to find and if possible revive Frederick's body.

He swam out following roughly the course his brother would have taken and in half an hour had reached the end of the western headland. To reach the spot giving access to the plateau he would have to round this point, but Gustav knew it was useless. The cage could not possibly have rounded the headland on its own and therefore his brother must have vanished between the headland and the camp, on exactly the course which he himself had just followed.

With a shock Gustav realized it was all over. There was nothing to be done to save Frederick now, and the memory of it would torment him forever. A desperate fury took hold of him. Why had he ever thought of coming to this island which now seemed to him as barbarous and inhospitable as it had in the first hours of their stay? He stared around him with disgust. The island was responsible for his brother's death and both of them had been deceived by it.

Gustav lost all idea of direction. He swam on with a cold voice inside him telling him there was no use in struggling any more. He felt his muscles tighten. The water was thundering in his head and his whole body seemed to rock with its impact. Why struggle any more? Salt was already filling his mouth and his nostrils. The sky seemed to be capsizing into the sea and Gustav began to sink, as though invisible hands were dragging him under.

He was still swimming but he no longer knew if he were alive or dead. Memories were coming and going in his brain as though he were falling asleep when suddenly he was struck by a crazy impossible idea that seemed to breathe new life into him. Without knowing how he did it,

Gustav found himself on the surface again and making for the point, which was only a few cables' lengths away. Gasping, he hauled himself onto a flat rock and sprawled there for a few moments without moving. Then he rose unsteadily to his feet, sustained by the intuition that had made him struggle again. He scanned the rocks and gave a cry. A dozen paces away lay his brother, pale but alive.

"I knew you'd come and find me," said Frederick.

On October 16, 1873, the British ship *Challenger* came in sight of Inaccessible Island while on a scientific mission in the South Atlantic, and her captain decided to take a look at the desert island.

A party went ashore, and when it returned some hours later Gustav and Frederick Stoltenhoff were in the ship's boat. A column of flames shot up from the beach where the brothers had set fire to their camp in a sort of frenzy before the astonished English sailors. They had fired their guns into the hut, trampled the garden and smashed their remaining penguins' eggs with pieces of driftwood until their faces were daubed with the sticky yolks. They had rushed headlong into the boat as if they were afraid that some mysterious power would catch them and force them to stay on the desolate island where the moaning of wind and sea greeted the oncoming night.

3

True-Life Robinson Crusoes

THE ferryboat dropped anchor a cable's length from the island and the passengers leaning over her sides saw a raft put out from the shore. On it were a man dressed in skins and a young boy holding a goat on a leash. The simple masquerade soon had the passengers laughing but it had taken them into the heart of the island's legend.

The scene was Más a Tierra, part of the Juan Fernández archipelago off the coast of Chile. Más a Tierra is a picturesque spot, with caves, rocky crags trickling with waterfalls, and warm deep bays. The Chileans are developing it as a tourist center.

It is purely as a tourist attraction that the man in skins embarks on his raft as each ferryboat approaches, and he is quite simply a reincarnation of Robinson Crusoe.

Since the hero of Daniel Defoe's *Robinson Crusoe* is an imaginary character and his island was in the South Atlantic near the mouth of the Orinoco River, not in the Pacific, there might seem very little connection between Robinson Crusoe and Juan Fernández. But the connection is this.

In 1711 a Scottish sailor about thirty-five years old disembarked from Woodes Rogers' ship the *Duke* in London. His name was Alexander Selkirk and several years later he was to publish the *Story of How Alexander Selkirk Lived for Four Years and Four Months Alone on a Desert Island*, a story which enjoyed considerable success.

Alexander Selkirk retired to Bristol where he told curious people who asked him questions that civilization had not made him forget his stay on the desert island. He was often to be seen wandering alone about the port, reliving his memories. In due course he resolved to interrupt his solitude by taking a wife, and being left a widower, he married again. He died in 1721 aged forty-five.

One of the most interested readers of Alexander Selkirk's story had been a sixty-year-old writer named Daniel Defoe, already well known as a journalist and pamphleteer who had had some disagreements with the Stuarts and the Church of England. Retired to the country and urgently in need of money, he saw in the story the inspiration for a novel. Defoe wrote *Robinson Crusoe* at a single stretch. It was published in 1719 and quickly sold out several editions.

Yet although *Robinson Crusoe* is an original work, bearing very little resemblance in detail to the Scottish sailor's experiences, the impression of absolute authenticity it gives the reader is the direct result of its basis in something that really happened.

On February 8, 1704, a small boat put out from the *Cinque Ports*, master Thomas Stradling, anchored off Más a Tierra. In the boat was one man. With him he had a few clothes, a mattress, a gun, some ammunition, tools, cooking utensils and a few books. The man was Alexander Selkirk, bosun of the *Cinque Ports*.

The boat was halfway to shore when it turned and came back to within hailing distance of the ship.

"Have you forgotten something?" called Stradling.

"No, I'm coming back," said Selkirk.

"Nothing doing. You wanted to land on your island, and land you shall, and stay there."

Relations between Selkirk and Stradling were strained. One day after a more than usually fierce argument in the course of which Stradling had announced that he could dispense with his services in the conduct of the ship, Selkirk had retorted that for his part he no longer wished to serve under such a captain and would leave the ship at Más a Tierra.

Selkirk did not believe his decision would have any serious consequences for himself, since the islands were used as a base by English and Spanish ships. It did not occur to him he would find any difficulty in boarding another vessel before very long.

All the same, when the time came to leave the *Cinque Ports* a momentary panic swept over him. Terror at the idea of living alone on a desert island, together with his suddenly seeing his departure in the light of desertion, made him turn back. But Stradling ordered him back to the island and Selkirk, knowing the man well enough to realize he would not give way, took up his oars again and rowed slowly to shore.

Más a Tierra is not a desolate land where castaways are liable to die. Goats, fish and vegetables provided Selkirk with ample sustenance. The Scottish seaman's tragedy was not that of hunger and thirst but of loneliness, which haunted him to the point where he was afraid to close his eyes for fear some strange peril would fall on him while he slept.

Awake, he forced himself not to think, and concentrated on building himself two huts. He hunted goats and, when he had used up all his powder and could no longer shoot them, he evolved a method of catching them on foot. He lit fires to prepare his food, but when he was no longer occupied, melancholy would overwhelm him.

Selkirk was sustained by the hope of sighting a ship and, in particular, Dampier's *St. George*, which had left England at the same time as the *Cinque Ports*; but the horizon remained empty. Selkirk found this hopeless waiting such a strain that there were times when he had to force himself not to look at the sea.

He would go into his hut and take up a book, usually the Bible, and read or sing the prayers and psalms aloud. He admitted afterward: "I was a better Christian in my loneliness than I had ever been or will be again."

Selkirk's only company was the cats left behind by various ships calling at Juan Fernández and which at the outset were a great assistance in freeing him from the rats that infested the place, destroying his food and clothing and even attacking him while he slept.

Soon Selkirk had tamed not only the cats but some kids as well, and he would sing and dance with them to amuse himself. But gradually it was Selkirk's own turn to be tamed by loneliness until, at the end of eight months, he had grown accustomed to his life and no longer missed the company of other people.

On February 2, 1708, Woodes Rogers' ship the *Duke* dropped anchor off Más a Tierra. A boat put in to shore and when it returned the seamen brought with them, besides a great quantity of shellfish, a man dressed in goatskins whose appearance was wilder than that of the goats themselves. It was Alexander Selkirk.

When Woodes Rogers questioned Selkirk he found he had difficulty in replying, for he had forgotten the use of speech. When at last he was able to make himself understood he told the captain his extraordinary story.

Woodes Rogers commented, "It must have been Providence that led you to disembark on this island."

"Why?" asked Selkirk.

"The *Cinque Ports* was wrecked soon after she left you here and nearly all her crew perished."

Alexander Selkirk was not the first man to live alone on Juan Fernández. In February 1616 six Dutch seamen from Jacob the Hermit's expedition found a refuge in the archipelago, and in 1681 an Indian sailor, called Robin, landed and lived there four years. Defoe may have heard of him, for his story was told in Dampier's memoirs which appeared in 1698, and it could even be in memory of this earlier castaway that he called his hero Robinson: the son of Robin.

57

Legends grow where they will. Alexander Selkirk's name is sure to live, but there are often no records of other men who have lived through even stranger and more thrilling adventures on desert islands than the Scottish sailor's. One such is Philip Ashton's on a tiny group of islands in the Antilles.

Philip Ashton was never to regret being a bachelor more than he did on a certain day in January 1722.

The day was a Saturday and his schooner was set on a course for Port Rossaway in Nova Scotia where he intended spending his money in enjoying himself after the long months at sea.

As they came into the harbor, a fresh northwesterly behind them, Ashton lifted his right arm from the tiller and pointed to the shore.

"We shan't be the only ones drunk tonight," he said to the four men of his crew, indicating a brig and a dozen fishing boats at their moorings. Their sails were lowered and the decks empty. The men must be already seated in the taverns of Port Rossaway, where the new arrivals might be sure of finding a warm welcome.

But no sooner had Philip Ashton's schooner hove to than a boat put out from the brig and steered toward the newcomers.

The schooner's boy waved cheerfully and called out, "We're going ashore. Just as soon as we're ready."

Down in his cabin Ashton finished shaving, inspected himself critically and went on deck congratulating himself on his new friends' eagerness. In his hands was a bottle of rum to celebrate the meeting. But as he emerged from the hatchway his face fell. The five men who stood before him all held cutlasses and pistols.

"Come here, you," said one of them roughly, pointing to Ashton.

Terrified, he obeyed.

"See the brig over there? Well, she's Ned Low's ship and he wants to see you."

Ashton's bottle of rum slipped from his fingers. He knew the name Ned Low only too well. The pirate had scourged the American coasts for many years.

"What does he want me for?" quavered Ashton.

Without offering a reply the man thrust his prisoners into the boat, which was soon alongside the brig. Ashton and his companions were taken aboard and five minutes later they heard heavy footsteps shaking the deck behind them. Turning they found themselves face to face with Ned Low.

He stood regarding them coldly, his face hard, his fingers curled around the stem of an empty pipe. Then he spoke.

At first Ashton did not understand him. His language was perfectly intelligible but the words themselves were so utterly unexpected that he could hardly grasp their meaning. The prisoners had been prepared for Ned Low to bluster and threaten and tell them their ship was his prize, but the pirate only asked one simple, pointless question.

"Are any of you married?"

The prisoners stared at each other, nonplused, while Ned Low repeated his question. Getting no reply, he drew his pistol and, holding it to Ashton's temple, yelled: "Well, you! Will you answer me? I asked if you were married?"

"No . . . no . . ." gasped Ashton.

"And your crew?"

"Nor are they."

Ned Low's fury left him. "I'm glad to know you're none of you married men," he said, seating himself on a coil of rope. "Because when a man's married . . ." He looked about vaguely as though talking to himself. "When a man's married . . ."

He did not finish the sentence but lowered his head, his face crumpling, and wiped his eyes on the back of his hand.

Ashton's astonishment grew. Ned Low, the terrible Ned Low whose path was strewn with fire and slaughter, was weeping.

He wept silently and sadly for a few moments then rose and went below, taking no further notice of his prisoners.

Ashton and his companions waited on deck in silence. They looked at the houses of Port Rossaway, seeing them as symbols of their lost freedom, then stared about them at the brig, at the sneering seamen polishing her guns, the ominous brown stains on her decks and the cuts and slashes on her bulwarks that spoke of former combats. And the captain of this ship of plunder and death had apparently captured them in order to ask whether they were married, and then gone away in tears. It was a nightmare, a frightful and absurd nightmare.

For Ashton this nightmare marked the beginning of an extraordinary adventure. Ned Low had asked if they were married because, knowing from his own experience that it was unlucky for a pirate to have ties ashore, he would have only unmarried men aboard his ship. His own wife had died in Boston giving birth to a son whom Low loved so dearly he could not think of the boy without tears. He knew the evils of such a weakness too well to tolerate it in any of his men.

Satisfied on this point, Ned Low decided to enroll Ashton and his men to complete his crew.

Ashton considered his strange fate. Because he had tried to forget his hard and monotonous life for a few days and because he was not a married man, he found himself forced to become an outlaw, to lead a life of robbery and murder until one day his own body would dangle from a yardarm.

He had pleaded with Ned Low, and even kneeled to him, but with no more effect than to rouse the pirate's suspicions.

Philip Ashton's intention was to escape as soon as the opportunity occurred. While the pirate brig beat about the Antilles, on the watch for the sails of a merchant ship, he was busy seeking for a way to accomplish it.

Often the cannon thundered over the sea, sometimes the signal that Ned Low had captured a prize, at others sending him running before the British corvettes. At these times Ashton shuddered with dread at the prospect of being taken, for he knew only too well he would hang with the rest of the pirates.

Three times he tried to make his escape and failed. Then, on March 9, 1723, he was one of a boat's crew sent to fetch water from a small island. Once on land Ashton made an excuse to go and look for coconuts, and hid himself.

He heard the voices of the seamen hunting for him, then these died away and the sound of oars grew fainter. When everything was quiet he knew he was alone and a free man once more.

But after a few hours Ashton's delight gave way to a gnawing anxiety as to how he was to live. He was without food or resources, he had no weapons to hunt game, and no tools. Anxiety turned to terror as the realization of his utter isolation came home to him. He was filled with an enormous sense of despondency, and sitting down under a tree he gave way to his misery.

Hunger roused him from his stupor and he stared up at the heavy palms hanging against the blue sky. Through a gap in the bushes where he lay hidden he could see Ned Low's vessel sailing slowly out to the open sea.

Ashton rose to his feet, his feelings a mixture of joy at his escape and forebodings as to his future. He picked a few berries and then set off to explore the island, which he estimated to be about twelve miles long, with fertile soil covered with vines, fig trees and coconut palms. Several times he startled a doe or a wild pig from a thicket but failed to hit them with the stick he carried.

He walked on under the sun. No weapons. No tools. No food. Every step beat out the same hopeless refrain. Once he stumbled over a pit covered with leaves and this gave him the idea of building a trap for game by disguising a hole with branches. He started digging at once but soon gave up, his hands bleeding.

Finally, when the pangs of hunger were tormenting his stomach, Ashton went back to the beach in the hope of finding crabs or other shellfish. He was disappointed. The beach was empty, but he noticed that here and there were smooth patches on the sand, as though the surface had been flattened by hand. Partly from curiosity and partly because he thought the pirates might have buried something there, he dug down and uncovered a pile of turtles' eggs.

Ashton swallowed several and, no longer in immediate fear of starvation, he lay down on the sand and fell asleep.

The next day, his food problem solved for the present, Ashton set about finding shelter. His hopes of finding a cave to live in were dashed, for the shore was hopelessly sandy. He turned inland with an idea of collecting branches and binding them together for the roof and walls of a hut.

Ashton had begun collecting his materials when he noticed three fallen moss-covered tree trunks. The logs looked solid and Ashton went toward them with the idea of dragging them down to the beach. He stopped short before he reached them, for the logs presented a curious appearance. The end of one looked like a caricature of a face with two small eyes and a large mouth. Ashton stared at it, half amused, half impressed, especially as a trick of the light made the mouth appear to be moving and the eyes opening.

It seems I shall have company, he was saying to himself with a smile, when suddenly the smile froze on his face and with a cry of alarm Ashton fled toward the beach, only stopping when he ran out of breath. The blood thundered in his head as he thought of his illusion that the tree had been stumbling toward him, like a mutilated human figure, its grisly mouth moving in voiceless threats. He was so terrified that a quarter of an hour passed before he was able to return and continue his work.

He approached the palms cautiously, watching for the

strange tree trunks, and again he drew back hastily. Three logs were definitely coming toward him.

Frightened as he was, Ashton stayed long enough to observe them and realized that what he had taken for tree trunks were in fact huge snakes, each of them a good ten feet long, basking in the sun.

Ashton avoided the palm groves for several days, until the necessity of building a hut forced him to return. The snakes were no longer in the same place, but he found others. They seemed harmless enough if kept at a distance and Ashton gradually grew used to their presence and learned to avoid them.

A month passed, then another, although Ashton scarcely noticed the passage of time. Without arms or implements he could not hunt or dig and he spent his days, when he had gathered fruit, shellfish and turtles' eggs, in exploring the island.

The place where he had landed was infested with tiny insects which plagued him night and day. Seeking a healthier place, Ashton boldly planned to reach an islet nearly two miles out to sea by swimmng, with the aid of a hollow bamboo as a sort of raft.

The islet was swept by the winds and clear of flies. Ashton made frequent excursions there. He would spend hours at a time stretched out on the sand, his mind empty of all ideas save a vague, half-conscious instinct for survival.

One morning as Ashton lay on the beach of the little island the sun suddenly broke through the clouds, burning his scantily clad body. He felt too weak to move; but an exceptionally large wave broke close to him, saturating him with its spray, and so roused him from his stupor. Pulling himself together he plunged into the sea and swam toward the larger island to take shelter under the trees.

His stiffened limbs moved reluctantly and his mind was still wandering. Only instinct drove him toward the island, where he waded painfully ashore, staggering on his blistered feet. The familiar surroundings seemed to have become hostile, the waving palms were a menace, and he was under the illusion that their trunks advanced on him like the serried ranks of an enemy army, while every animal cry made him shiver.

Suddenly Ashton heard a harsh grunting that grew louder as it approached. A wild boar was bearing down on him, churning up a cloud of dust and sand as it came.

Ashton gave a cry of fear. Too weak to run, he was ready to be torn to pieces by the boar when he saw a low-hanging branch and swung himself off the ground, only just in time. After making several thrusts with its head at emptiness, the boar lost interest and vanished into the forest.

Ashton sank to the ground sobbing. This attack seemed to him a proof that there was no home for him on the island.

There is a moment in the life of every Robinson Crusoe when his desert island becomes an enemy. This moment had come for Ashton, and he regretted he had ever deserted Ned Low's ship. He had feared being caught and hanged by the English, yet that had been no more than a risk, whereas now his fate was certain—death on this unknown shore, cut off from the world.

Ashton stood up. Slowly a terror he could not fight down was mastering him and driving him relentlessly toward the sea. The long, curling waves crept in toward him as though seeking him out. Still Ashton walked on until the cool water lapping round his bleeding feet revived him a little. His eye wandered over the sea and he gave a cry. There, two hundred yards from the shore, was a canoe with a man sitting in it. His face was half hidden in a matted gray beard and there was a fur hat on his head. He sat quite still watching Ashton's ghostlike figure wading into the water.

Ashton and the newcomer stared at one another, each believing himself the victim of a delusion. At the sound of Ashton's voice the stranger raised his hand but he did not take up his paddle. It was clear he was seeking a refuge on the island Ashton was preparing to leave and was afraid he had fallen in with a gang of pirates.

Still the stranger hesitated. At last he made up his mind and hailed Ashton, and a few minutes later the canoe was scraping on the sand.

The stranger leaped out, surveyed Ashton, who still kept silent, and quickly made up his mind he was not dangerous. Completely reassured, he grasped Ashton's wasted hand.

"Glad to meet you," said the newcomer. "Who are you?"

"My name is Ashton. I have lived here for nine months."

"For nine months?"

"Yes, I escaped from a pirate vessel."

The stranger nodded and said nothing. Ashton waited for him to announce his own identity but he only said, "I come from a long way away. From England. From the north of England. I left it a very long time ago, twenty-two years ago."

"Don't you want to go back?"

"It's too late now, much too late."

He was silent for a moment as though occupied with some inner reverie, then sighed.

"I should think myself lucky to be alive. The Spaniards were going to burn me."

"Burn you? Why?"

The stranger made a vague gesture.

"It doesn't matter now that I'm safe."

Ashton dared not press him. He felt both wonder and fear and also a kind of sympathy for the old man who was a fugitive like himself and whose chance appearance had saved his life. His company would make life easier to bear, especially as he possessed a dog, a gun and ammunition as well as the canoe.

Ashton's life did indeed become more bearable. The stranger killed wild pigs and the meat put strength into Ashton. He began to hope again, and although he exchanged few words with his taciturn companion he drew comfort simply from his presence.

Two days after he had come, the old man set off again on a hunting expedition to a nearby island where he hoped the game would be more plentiful. Ashton's feet were still painful and made walking difficult, so he was forced to stay.

"I'll be back in a few hours," promised the other as he stepped into the canoe.

In the evening a storm blew up. Although Ashton tended a fire on the shore all night as a signal to the canoe, the old man did not return. When the sun rose over a calm sea Ashton knew he had vanished as strangely as he had come.

He examined the things the stranger had left him: a reserve of salt pork, a knife, some powder and tobacco. Thanks to the knife he could now cut up turtles and shellfish and make spears for hunting. His wounds were healing and he was again in good health.

Some weeks after the old man's disappearance Ashton saw a black speck on the sea and watched with a thumping heart, hoping it was a sign that his companion had managed to find his way back to the island. The speck soon resolved itself into a canoe, driven toward the coast by the tide, but when it reached the beach he found that it was empty. Whether it was the old stranger's boat or another that had drifted away from some shipwreck, Ashton never discovered, but he looked on it as a gift from heaven. With a boat he could escape from the island.

His first venture was to explore the archipelago in the hope of meeting with a ship, but he returned from the expedition in a hurry. He had sighted a ship but as he was on the point of hailing her had made out the skull and cross-bones at her masthead.

After this he resumed his solitary existence until June 1724, when he was joined on the island by some inhabitants of Honduras Bay seeking refuge from the Spaniards. The newcomers treated him as a friend and put all their resources at his disposal, and Ashton told himself his troubles were at an end. These men are armed, he thought, and even if pirates were to attack us we should be able to defend ourselves.

He was wrong. Pirates attacked their company while on a hunting expedition to a nearby island and routed them. Ashton succeeded in making his escape with one companion and they reached Honduras Bay, abandoned by the Spaniards, at the very moment an English ship put into the harbor. The *Diamond*'s captain was willing to take his compatriot aboard and, three years after his capture by Ned Low, Ashton returned home where, in his own words, he was welcomed like a man returned from the dead.

Alexander Selkirk lived on his desert island for four years, and Philip Ashton for two, but a Spanish seaman, Pedro Serrano, lived for seven years, from 1540 to 1547, on a rocky island off the coast of Peru.

Less fortunate than Selkirk, Serrano was washed up after the wreck of his ship on a completely barren and waterless island. Rainfall was high and he hoarded water in upturned turtle shells and, in the absence of any form of shelter, had no alternative but to take to the sea when the sun was too hot. He lived on fish and seaweed as well as turtle meat and managed to light a fire to cook them, with flint and a sort of tinder he contrived from the threads of his shirt.

Serrano does not seem to have suffered from the melancholy that afflicted the more sensitive Selkirk, although his only occupation apart from fishing was searching the horizon for signs of a passing ship. During three years he sighted half a dozen but, despite his frantic signals, none of them turned off its course because there were many dangerous reefs and shoals in the area. It was as a result of these dangers that Serrano found himself no longer alone on his rock.

One morning he saw a figure staggering on the sand, the only survivor of the crew of a ship which had foundered during the night. The man had swum ashore and he came toward Serrano, thinking him to be one of his comrades who had also escaped from the wreck. When he saw the hairy creature with its brown, grimy skin and matted beard he turned and stumbled away in terror, whereupon Serrano also took fright and ran and hid himself at the opposite end of the island. For a long time both uttered prayers to heaven until, hearing each other calling on the name of Jesus Christ, they were reassured, and each admitted they had thought the other an incarnation of the devil.

The two men settled down to life together, although they sometimes quarreled so violently that they lived for months without speaking. They were always on the verge of madness and, if a ship had not arrived at the island, would doubtless eventually have completely lost their reason.

A ship did come at last and lowered a boat. It came toward the shore where Serrano and his companion, with tears of joy, were ready to embark. Then without warning it turned back to the ship, the sailors being so terrified at the sight of them that they refused to take such monsters aboard.

Serrano shrieked prayers and entreaties at the sailors and succeeded in convincing them they were dealing with human beings.

When he returned to Europe Serrano was granted an audience by Charles V, who gave him a pension which the seaman never lived to enjoy. He died a few months after his rescue.

The attitude of the sailors who rescued Serrano is not as strange as it may seem. Superstitions often attached to desert islands, which were believed to have a curse on them, or to be haunted by ghosts or monsters who resented intruders.

Around about the year 1515, seamen crossing the South Atlantic believed in such a legend. They told how if any landed on the island of St. Helena, which was then uninhabited, they would be greeted by a species of monster which was covered in rags and had a horrible caricature of a human face without ears or nose, always keeping at a distance from the sailors, who on their part were too overcome with revulsion to go near it.

However, the creature did not seem to bear strangers any malice; indeed it would leave them casks of fresh water, fruit, vegetables and pork or goat's meat before disappearing. The sailors would take the provisions on board and depart, none of them ever having the courage to approach the frightful yet kindly monster.

At last the captain of a Portuguese vessel, determined to get to the bottom of the mystery, dropped anchor at St. Helena with every intention of discovering the truth of the story, which he believed was simply a quarter-deck yarn, invented by the seamen.

Looking at the island before going ashore, the captain was amazed to see a figure laying out victuals and making signs with a cloth. He ordered out the longboat and as it drew in to the beach the creature—they could hardly tell if it was a man—stood staring at the boat, then turned and fled swiftly behind some bushes.

The captain climbed the beach with a handful of sailors, whom he took the precaution of arming, and began searching the bushes where the stranger had vanished, but neither the search nor their shouts yielded any result. While he was hesitating which way to go the captain noticed some tracks and followed them, although with some difficulty, as they were often lost among rocks and undergrowth. After a while one of the seamen gave a shout, pointing to an opening in the hillside sixty yards away. As the party approached they were able to make out a narrow cave with the embers of a wood fire smoking outside it.

The captain walked on alone. At first he saw nothing but shadows, then, in a deep niche in the cave, he distinguished a dreadful face. It was undoubtedly human but the nose and ears had been cut off and the ghastly mutilated visage was framed in long matted hair.

The man seemed to feel no fear at the sight of the captain but only a great surprise, as though he were confronted with someone from another world. He was apparently struggling to understand why anyone should go out of his way to see him. After several minutes had passed in silence he spoke, slowly and hoarsely in Portuguese.

"Have you come to take me back?"

"I have only come to pay you a visit and thank you for the victuals. Are you Portuguese?"

"You swear by almighty God you have not come to take me back?"

"Certainly. You are free to do as you wish. But tell me why you are here."

"As a punishment for my sins," said the man.

"Were your sins so dreadful?"

The man nodded and told the captain his story. His name

was Fernão Lopes and he had emigrated from Portugal to Goa in the Indies. In 1510 the town was taken by Albuquerque, who treated the inhabitants, in his usual fashion, with the utmost cruelty. Discovering that in order to further their interests certain of his compatriots had been converted to Islam, he ordered their noses and ears to be cut off and sent them back to Portugal. Among them was Fernão Lopes.

When the ship taking the unfortunates back to their native land called at St. Helena, Lopes and several of his companions were ordered to go ashore and fill the casks with fresh water. Lopes had wept and moaned continuously since his mutilation, not because of his physical sufferings but because he could not bear the idea of returning to Portugal a despised cripple, probably reduced to begging for his living. Without pausing to consider that he was risking his life by remaining on St. Helena, he ran off and hid himself until the ship sailed.

Discovering his prisoner's absence, the captain left some food and clothing on the shore, but he had no illusions as to the fate which awaited Lopes. He would die slowly on the uninhabited island.

But the captain was wrong. Once he had recovered his liberty and was no longer haunted by the nightmare of shame awaiting him in Portugal, Lopes gained fresh strength. He wanted to live and would live in spite of everything.

He found pigs and goats on the island and abandoned vegetable patches, witnesses perhaps to the passing of some freebooter, and was soon not merely assured against death from starvation but possessed of a surplus with which he

73

resolved to benefit any ships that called at the island. It seemed to him this would be a way of atoning for his sins.

The Portuguese captain who had discovered his retreat listened to Lopes' story in amazement. "How long have you been here?" he asked.

"Two years."

"You have really no desire to return to Portugal?"

"Not for anything in the world, I have told you."

"I cannot compel you. But as you do good to ships I will leave you fruit and vegetable seeds and a few chickens. Before very long you will be a godsend to sailors if they can be sure of finding fresh food in mid-Atlantic."

Lopes' farming prospered, and gradually St. Helena became a regular port of call for ships' captains who benefited, as well as satisfying their curiosity, until the name of Fernão Lopes became so well known that the King of Portugal, Emanuel the Fortunate, expressed a wish to meet the former renegade who had made himself the kindly hermit of a desert island.

His reception by the king at Lisbon was Lopes' revenge on fate. A few years earlier he would have stepped ashore in chains among a miserable crowd of prisoners, now he was welcomed by the authorities and publicly thanked by the king for the services he had rendered to sailors.

Assuming that Lopes would wish to remain in Portugal, the king promised him a pension to supply his needs and was astonished when the hermit thanked him profusely but refused the offer.

"But surely you cannot wish to go back to St. Helena?" exclaimed the king.

Yes, Fernão Lopes wanted to go back to his island. The

answer seemed so inconceivable to Emanuel that he told Lopes to think the matter over and give him his answer in a month's time. When the time was up and Lopes still asked to return, as if he were begging a favor, the king consented.

"At least you know there will be a welcome for you in Portugal whenever you decide to renounce your hermitage," he said.

But Fernão Lopes never left his island. At his death in 1546 he had lived for thirty-four years on St. Helena.

The monster of St. Helena was never heard of again and the island lost its reputation for being haunted. But eight hundred miles to the north lay another island, Ascension, and this too had an evil reputation in the seventeenth century, especially after the famous navigator, Dampier, had been all but wrecked on its reefs. Superstitious sailors avoided the island because, although uninhabited, the island was supposedly peopled with demons.

"In the dead of night of June 16th, after making my customary round, I found myself surrounded by strange noises, sounds of mingled curses, blasphemies and obscenities. I trembled lest I should fall victim to some monster since for whom but myself could the devil have left his home and come to create this hell on earth? One of the devils, more active than the rest, was continuously lashing my face with his tail. . . ."

We have already had a glimpse of the hazards that await man on a desert island, of his struggles against fear, melancholy, hunger and thirst, heat and cold, but this is the first time we have seen him confronted with the devil. Yet this was the fate of a Dutch seaman who, in punishment of some crime, was put ashore on Ascension Island, with only a cask of water, some food and a pistol, on May 5, 1725.

For the majority of castaways, however desolate their desert island may be, it represents safety and their only chance of survival. Knowing this helps them to bear their sufferings, fosters their ingenuity and gives them courage to wait hopefully and patiently for rescue. The Dutchman's position was different. For him the island was neither a haven nor a refuge from society, but an instrument of punishment. In his eyes its harsh terrain represented a terrible retribution before which he was helpless and tormented. He did not rebel against it or protest his punishment was undeserved, but on the contrary accepted it and admitted its justice.

"I began to reflect seriously upon my misspent life and on the justice of the Almighty who had seen fit to punish me in such an exemplary fashion for my unworthy crimes," he wrote, and this consciousness of his guilt, however praiseworthy, was almost his undoing.

Yet the instinct of self-preservation was strong, and the sailor soon gave up lamenting his lot and began considering how he was to live. He hunted birds, fished for turtles and shellfish, gathered herbs and roots, and he raised a signal on a headland to attract the attention of passing ships. Unfortunately, unless for urgent repairs, ships avoided Ascension; the island's arid climate and lack of water made it uninviting.

Whenever he was not busy the seaman was overcome by fresh remorse. At night as he lay sleepless between nightmares he would start up, sweating, in the belief that invis-

ible beings were attacking him. He began to be haunted by
demons once more. The wretched man would hear voices
cursing him in the darkness, filling his tent with a clamor
that turned his flesh cold as an Egyptian mummy's, and he
even saw the ghost of a dead friend. When dawn came he
seized his prayer book and read aloud from it, hoping by
so doing to drive away the evil spirits. Then he set out on
his daily search, not for food, for there was plenty on the
island, but for water.

All that remained of his store was about a gallon of thick
and foul-smelling liquid. The clouds that sometimes passed
over the island never broke in rain and he searched hopelessly for a spring until his feet were bleeding. At last, after
seeking for a week, he found one and drank so deeply that
for a time he was almost drunk with water. He filled every
vessel he possessed but even so, when he returned to the
spring a few days later, a tremor ran through him. It had
dwindled to a mere trickle of water that would soon cease
altogether.

Once more he suffered agonies of thirst. Occasionally he
would find a pool but it always dried up very quickly. At
first he thought this was due to the sun, but when he found
that all the pools ran dry as mysteriously as the first, he began to imagine himself the victim of the evil demons who
haunted his nights and worked to hasten his death. In reality the guilty creatures were the herds of wild goats which
roamed about the island seeking like him to quench
their thirst.

He was convinced his end was near when one evening a
skeleton appeared in the entrance to the cave where he had
made his home in order to escape from the wind that pen-

etrated his tent. It came toward him pointing with its index finger at its throat.

"He means to tell me I shall die of thirst," moaned the seaman, burying himself in his blanket, from which he dared not emerge until the sun was high in the sky.

With the stubbornness of desperation he continued his exploration of the island, looking for the gleam of water and following the trail of the goats to see where they drank.

From time to time, when he lay down wearily on the sand, he would hear the invisible cursing and swearing around him in the darkening air. The figure of a man who had been the companion of his evil days seemed to approach and abuse him and then vanished.

His delirium was only the beginning of his sufferings. For a few more weeks he held out, drinking turtles' blood and urine, a perpetual prey to ghostly visions. "I have become a walking skeleton . . ." he noted in the diary he still struggled to keep every day.

Six months later his skeleton was found by Captain Mawson of the *Compton.*

So not all Robinson Crusoes have won their struggles for survival on desert islands, as did Selkirk, Serrano, Fernão Lopes, and others, such as John Jewitt in 1803, the only survivor when his ship's crew were massacred by Indians; Daniel Foss who lived for five years, from 1809 to 1813, on an island in the Pacific; and the Englishman Timmins, who was cast up on a Pacific atoll in 1914 after his ship went down and not rescued until 1925; and many others still in the long list of miraculous escapes from desert islands.

But there is another list, a much longer one, of those

who did not come home, which includes those who tried to find asylum on antarctic islands swept by icy gales, as well as on the pleasant lands that lie under the South Pacific sun. All these are the ocean's victims whom islands have not saved but only granted a few weeks' or a few months' respite; and they make up the invisible inhabitants of the mysterious island kingdoms.

4

Uncrowned Kings and
Buried Treasure

"I DREAM of sailors forgotten on an island. . . ."
Once again truth and fiction meet. When Baudelaire
was writing this poem, the *Annales Maritimes* published an
article estimating that several hundred sailors of all nation-
alities who had been presumed drowned were in fact still
alive, lost in the South Seas.

Some were castaways from shipwrecks but by far the
greater number had left their ships of their own accord for
the sake of adventure. What were they looking for? Fortune, perhaps, but certainly freedom and the chance of
such a fantastic piece of luck as that of Joseph Kabris, half
a century earlier.

On an evening in May 1793 the naval brig *Dumouriez* was tacking in a slack breeze down the calm waters of the Gironde. On board were a number of volunteers for the young republic, and among them was a lad of fourteen named Joseph Kabris, the cabin boy. It was his first voyage.

Eight days later, off Cape Finisterre, the *Dumourez* engaged a Spanish galleon. There was a short battle, the galleon yielded and the French brig made for Bordeaux with her prize. One morning shortly after daybreak the *Dumouriez* was surprised by an English squadron and although she put up a brave fight was forced to surrender in her turn.

Her crew was taken prisoner and sent to the prison hulks at Portsmouth, where poor little Joseph Kabris brooded miserably on his fate. He had dreamed of a free life on the ocean wave and now he was shut up in an airless barrack where his only contact with the sea was the constant suck and gurgle of the foul, evil-smelling water in the inner harbor of Portsmouth.

Six months dragged by, each day drearier than the last, and often as Kabris thought of escape, he knew it was hopeless without a boat to enable him to cross the Channel. Some men succeeded in getting away but no one ever knew what had become of them.

As time passed, Kabris grew more sick of the filth, the starvation and vermin among which he lived, until he was ready to take any chance of freedom. Then one day the prisoners were taken in turn before a visitor who, to their surprise, turned out to be a Frenchman, an *émigré* officer.

"I am offering you your liberty," he told them, and explained that a landing on the French coast was planned with the help of the British fleet and they needed men. "You have only to sign and you will be free."

Kabris was ready to agree to almost anything if it meant escape from the rotting hulks, and as his republican sympathies were in any case no more than lukewarm, he engaged himself to go.

The night of July 16, 1795, found him with a party landing on the French coast near Quiberon Bay, but he had not fired more than a few shots before he heard the signal to retreat. By now, as he stumbled back to the dark beach amid a confusion of noise, shrieks and explosions, Kabris was beginning to regret having mixed himself up in the business. He saw no sign of a boat and so plunged straight into the sea and swam for several hours before he at last reached an English ship just as it was on the point of sailing.

Back in England, he found himself in the doubly unenviable position of ex-prisoner of war and out-of-work seaman. One day, in a Portsmouth tavern, he learned that a certain Captain Knight was recruiting a crew for a voyage of exploration in the South Seas. Hurrying down to the quay, Kabris boarded a stoutly built whaling vessel where Captain Knight, who needed men, engaged him on the spot.

In the spring of 1796 the ship sailed from England, and two years later there were vague rumors that she had been lost in the South Seas. She was believed to have gone aground on the reefs of the Marquesas, and it was off these islands that two men were washed up, clinging to some broken spars, in the summer of 1797. The men were Joseph Kabris and an Englishman named Roberts, the only survivors of Knight's crew.

They crawled on to the beach and dragged themselves wearily up the burning sand into the meager shade of the palms, where they fell asleep.

When they awoke they were surrounded by a crowd of grinning savages, their faces and bodies painted with weird designs. Joseph Kabris and his companion were prisoners.

These islanders were the terror of merchant adventurers in the South Seas and many had perished on their sacrificial altars. Such was the fate in store for Joseph Kabris, for the king of the tribe into whose hands he had fallen decreed he was to be sacrificed on the summit of a nearby hill, known as Mount Palisade.

Kabris was locked in a hut and waited fearfully for his executioners. One morning a plumed native whom Kabris recognized as the chief of the tribe opened the door of the hut. He was accompanied by a crop-headed young woman, her neck ornamented with an assortment of charms, and both of them regarded Kabris in silence for some minutes, then departed.

The next day the woman returned alone and on the following day Kabris was taken out of the hut. He was loaded with ornaments and compelled to take part in a ceremony of alternate songs and dances. Kabris believed these were the preparations for his sacrifice but at the end of the ceremony he was surprised to find himself, not merely still alive, but married to the king's daughter, the girl who had visited him in the hut.

Making the best of the situation in which he found himself, Kabris adopted the customs of the tribe and even allowed himself to be tattooed. He distinguished himself so greatly in battles with neighboring tribes that the chieftain named him his successor in admiration of his prowess. In less than two years Kabris, under the name of Kabrili, was monarch of Nuka Hiva Island.

The erstwhile seaman from Bordeaux took his role very seriously and rapidly established his authority over his subjects. He never forgot his origins and welcomed kindly any white men, usually fishermen, whom chance brought to Nuka Hiva.

On May 10, 1804, the king learned that "two great canoes" had dropped anchor off the islands. They were the *Nadjedja* and the *Neva*, the ships of the Russian explorer, Krusenstern, on his journey around the world. Eager to display his royal pomp before Europeans, Kabrili made a state visit to Krusenstern and, gaining confidence from his delight at once more speaking to a civilized person, he told him his story.

Kabrili ordered a magnificent feast in honor of his guests and in return Krusenstern invited Kabrili on board. During the meal the king suddenly asked to be taken back to Europe.

"Do you want to leave Nuka Hiva?" asked Krusenstern in surprise.

"No," was the reply. "I want to interest the French government in the island. I need financial help to realize the worth of Nuka Hiva."

"Aren't you afraid your subjects will forget you?"

"They will wait ten years if need be for the riches I have promised them."

84

After a moment's hesitation Krusenstern agreed, and on May 14, 1804, they set sail.

Kabris was sincere in his desire to interest France in Nuka Hiva but he was also eager to make use of his royal title and find himself, once a common seaman and a miserable prisoner on the Portsmouth hulks, honored and admired.

Krusenstern dropped anchor at Kronstadt on August 7, 1806. Kabris went straight to St. Petersburg where he begged an audience with Alexander I.

Weeks passed. Reverting to his name of Kabrili, Kabris lived in a poor hotel on the outskirts of the city and presented himself regularly at the palace in the hope of being received. At length, tired of this persistent potentate, the Czar agreed to see him for a few moments out of curiosity.

He listened to his story and then dismissed him, with a promise to have him sent to France as soon as possible.

Alexander had recently concluded the Peace of Tilsit with Napoleon and Kabrili hoped he would soon be in Paris, but the Czar forgot him. The king of Nuka Hiva lived from hand to mouth, finding a job as a swimming instructor in St. Petersburg and beginning to long for the sunny South Seas.

Day after day Kabrili dreamed of his lost island. He forgot the boredom which had grown on him among the islanders and his homesickness and remembered only his kingship, the authority he held over thousands of people, and the feeling of power he experienced in command and government.

He was forced to be patient. Russia was once more at war with France, but after the fall of Napoleon he again began badgering the Russian authorities to send him back to France. At long last, on June 26, 1817, he landed at Calais.

In France Kabrili reverted to his royal title again. He dressed himself as a native of Nuka Hiva in order to appeal to people's imagination and went to Paris to seek an audience with King Louis. He was presented to the Duc de Richelieu, who procured him an audience with the king, and although the interview was very brief the former seaman had the satisfaction of seeing himself treated with all the ceremony due to a foreign head of state. But Kabrili's hopes of interesting France in Nuka Hiva were doomed to disappointment. The French government had other matters on its hands, and all he could obtain was a promise to send him back to his island whenever a French ship should be sailing for the Pacific.

Kabrili traveled to Bordeaux to see his parents, but his father and mother were both dead. Without money or family he was destitute and in despair of ever seeing his kingdom again, when a traveling showman proposed he join his circus, giving him the idea of returning to Nuka Hiva with the money he earned.

Kabrili accepted the offer. Nicknamed "The Tattooed King," he explained to gaping onlookers that he had agreed to show himself to the public only to procure the means to buy the necessary tools to develop his country's resources.

After Paris "The Tattooed King" exhibited himself in traveling fairs all over northern France. Kabrili began to sink into apathy. He was greedy for honor and respect but, for all his naïve pride at having become king of his far-away islands, he only met with the vulgar curiosity of the crowd. He lived on in the hope of one day returning to Nuka Hiva, but it was not to be. In March 1824 he collapsed after a performance and was taken to a hospital, suffering from pneumonia. He died a week later, with only the ghosts of his lost island beside him in his delirium.

Kabris's adventure was by no means an unusual one. In March 1883 another castaway lay stretched on the sandy shore of Yap, one of the most westerly of the Caroline Islands. He was a seaman from the American bark *Belvedere* and he too was captured by islanders and taken to their village.

The sailor, whose name was David O'Keefe, had no illusions as to his fate. He knew the inhabitants of the Carolines were cannibals and not noted for sparing any white men who fell into their hands. But he was amazed to find himself left at liberty, given food and a hut to live in, and treated with great respect.

A miracle, thought O'Keefe, who had expected to be slaughtered out of hand. The miracle had a simple explanation.

Among certain tribes there was a belief that dead men were reincarnated in others, not necessarily of the same color. Seeing the mysterious white man come from the sea, the natives believed they were in the presence of one of these and it was their duty to honor him.

David O'Keefe lived on Yap Island, becoming accustomed to the islanders' way of life, until he too, like Joseph Kabris, married the chieftain's daughter, despite the fact that he already had a wife in the United States. On the chief's death O'Keefe was elected king of Yap, and he did not neglect to feather his own nest. Whenever a trading vessel was sighted he would put out in a canoe and hail her, offering to sell her captain a quantity of nacre or copra. As often as not the captain accepted, and Yap became a regular rendezvous for merchant adventurers in the South Seas.

In this way eighteen years went by, until one day O'Keefe began to feel homesick and made up his mind the time had come to return to America. By boarding a schooner calling at Yap he could reach Hong Kong and from China have no trouble in finding a boat bound for America.

O'Keefe should have reached Hong Kong in March 1902 but nothing was heard of him, and it was at first thought he must have picked up a vessel bound directly for San Francisco. When months passed and there was still no word it was assumed he must have perished in a typhoon.

A year later the San Francisco courts received a strange letter from O'Keefe's widow. This lady, his legitimate wife, had thought him dead until she received a letter through a sailor in which her husband told her of his life in Yap and announced his return. But this return never took place. Mrs. O'Keefe had inquiries made and learned that O'Keefe had left his "kingdom" on his way to the United States and, deducing from this that her husband had been lost at sea, she filed a petition claiming the goods he had amassed in Yap.

In theory her claim was well founded but it raised a number of legal problems, since the goods were in foreign territory, the Caroline Islands having been sold to Germany by Spain in 1899. There were long legal proceedings. The new chief of Yap who had succeeded David O'Keefe maintained that the American seaman had taken all his possessions with him when he left the island. The most he would undertake was to supply the widow's needs if she chose to reside in Yap.

Mrs. O'Keefe's surprise at hearing her husband had become a king was equaled by that of the mayor of a small village near Mauléon in the Pyrenees when in 1930 he received a letter informing him that one of his villagers who had left the district a dozen years before had become king of a tiny island in the Galápagos group, which he bequeathed to his native village.

The inhabitants appreciated their fellow villager's generosity but none of them felt any wish to take possession of the legacy and add one more to the number of uncrowned kings who now and then stranded themselves on some remote stretch of land where they could feel the illusion of imaginary royalty.

Other uncrowned kings were Van Ramondt of Tintamare Island; Archibald C. Everett of Arorae in the Gilbert Islands; Martin C. Harman of Lindy Island; and Jean Terret on his island off the coast of Brazil. Some may call them megalomaniacs but others will see in them victims of the subtle, eternal island magic. Another facet of the same enchantment is the lure of buried treasure.

"The treasure . . . save the treasure. . . ."
The date was March 15, 1845, and the scene the deck of a Spanish schooner in the Pacific Ocean, some four hun-

89

dred miles from Costa Rica, within sight of Cocos Island. The schooner's captain was bending over a man who had just been dragged exhausted from the sea where he had been floating half-unconscious, gripping a broken spar.

He lay on the deck, turning his head away from the glaring sunlight, and murmuring broken sentences in which the word "treasure" frequently recurred.

"He's raving," said a seaman.

The captain made a gesture for silence. He was trying to follow the rescued man's words but the disjointed phrases hardly rose above a whisper and he soon gave it up, deciding to question the man further when he recovered.

He was anxious to discover the truth about his curious castaway, for it was a story he already knew in part. He had sailed those seas for many years and knew by reputation the island whose blue outline rose above the horizon. Tradition said there was treasure buried there.

The reader may smile but it is a fact that, just as *Robinson Crusoe* has its basis in truth, so Robert Louis Stevenson's *Treasure Island* is borne out by actual events.

For three centuries the Spanish Plate Fleet, bringing the riches of the New World to Europe, was a target for pirates. After carrying out one of their many successful attacks on a treasure-laden galleon, the plunderers had to solve the tricky problem of where to stow their booty in safety.

Had they chosen a known port it would have been swiftly blockaded by warships, so it was essential to find secret harbors where they could hoard their plunder, preferably on some uncharted island far out in the ocean.

Chests containing gold and silver plate, coins, jewels and precious stones were stowed in carefully hidden caches, known only to the chief and a few of his henchmen.

Often the pirates were captured before they could recover their spoils, and so it comes about that on many distant islands, still perhaps uninhabited, there is the hidden treasure that fills the dreams and ambitions of adventurers.

Legend has it Cocos Island was one of these, and this was why the captain of the Spanish schooner felt reasonably sure the strange man he had rescued was connected with a treasure-hunting expedition.

When the man recovered consciousness he said in answer to the captain's questions that his name was Keating and he was trading along the coast when his ship struck a reef off Cocos Island, broke up and sank with no other survivors.

"You kept talking about treasure when we picked you up," the captain reminded him. "Precious stones and such."

"I didn't know what I was saying," said Keating. "I was delirious."

"Why do you think those things came into your mind?"

Keating paused before replying.

"I seem to remember on the evening before the wreck we had been joking about the Cocos Island treasure," he said at last, adding confidently, "It's only a legend, of course."

The captain regarded him closely.

"A legend?"

"Isn't it?"

"If we only knew . . ." said the captain.

"You don't really believe . . . ?"

"I'm not saying what I believe. But a hundred years ago pirates used the island."

"What makes you think they might have buried treasure there?"

"I think it perfectly possible. But if there is a treasure it would be very difficult to locate. The pirates are bound to have taken good care of that."

Keating only nodded, apparently unconvinced, and the captain let the matter drop. He was sure Keating was hiding something, that he was one of those who had tried their luck on Cocos Island.

Occasionally men with a feverish glint in their eyes could be seen on the quays at Costa Rica asking for a ship to take them to Cocos Island. There was no need to ask them questions, for the fever burning in their veins was the lust for gold, though none of them ever found the treasure they were after. I'm certain now, it doesn't exist, thought the captain.

On one point he was right. Keating was certainly after treasure but the captain was quite wrong in assuming it was not to be found. Keating had found it only the day before he was shipwrecked.

Keating was a Canadian and came from Newfoundland. He had obtained a map marking the exact hiding place of the treasure from an old sailor, and had immediately fitted out a ship in partnership with a few others to go and hunt for it. As to what had passed between the vessel's arrival at the island and the moment when the Spanish captain fished the half-drowned Keating out of the sea, there is only his own story as he told it to his partners in Canada, for evidence.

"I found the treasure," he told them. They asked where it was and his face hardened.

"My men were not to be trusted. I should have suspected something. They mutinied the day after we reached the island, put up to it by the bosun, and Captain Brogue and myself were locked up."

"What did they hope to gain?"

"The treasure, of course. I would have promised them a share but I had no guarantee they wouldn't kill us as soon as we found it.

"One night when they were all dead drunk Brogue and I escaped through a porthole, lowered away a boat and landed on the island. The directions on the map were quite clear and we started digging at dawn."

In a few hours Keating and Brogue had uncovered the Cocos Island treasure. They loaded as much as she would hold into the boat and quickly put to sea with the idea of making for Costa Rica, but they had not gone very far when they struck some concealed rocks. Their boat was badly holed and sank like a stone. Keating was picked up many hours later by the Spanish schooner but there was no trace of Brogue.

For years Keating lived in Newfoundland dreaming of his lost treasure. He would spend hours on end gazing at the horizon to where, far beyond the gray Atlantic, lay a green island caught between the blue of sea and sky. Then one day he suddenly began preparations for a second expedition and set about recruiting fresh partners, promising "all those who join in the venture an assured sufficiency for life." A friend whose name was Hackett was prepared to back him and found him a ship, but Keating died only a few months before the date fixed for departure.

Is there any truth in the story? It contains much that is doubtful and contradictory. The tale of the mutiny is plausible enough in itself, but it is hard to imagine how Keating seriously believed he could reach Costa Rica in a heavily laden boat without being pursued and captured by the mutinous seamen. Moreover, if it was true, as he claimed, that the bulk of the treasure had gone to the bottom of the sea, either there must have been enough still left on the island to warrant a second expedition or Keating must have known of a second hoard.

Yet another riddle is the fate of the ship in which he originally reached the island. The mutineers would most probably have made a search for the treasure before leaving, but their destination is a mystery. The ship was never seen again.

For many more years Cocos Island was visited by adventurers, but they were simply gamblers, not equipped for a large-scale treasure hunt, and soon gave up the quest.

However, in 1896, there was an expedition with a more professional appearance. A warship, flying the red ensign and bearing on her prow the name *Haughty*, lay at anchor off the island. Her decks were almost empty. Nearly every man of the crew was ashore and from time to time the shattering roar of an explosion would send a cloud of dust and smoke into the shimmering air. There was a clatter of picks and shovels as the seamen, stripped to the waist, toiled in the craters left by the blasting. An officer stood by giving directions. He was Commander Shrapnel of the *Haughty* who was making his bid for treasure.

After eight days he sailed away empty-handed and on his return to England found the Lords of the Admiralty displeased at having Her Majesty's ships used for private purposes. He was dismissed from the service.

Shrapnel's only comment was that he had in any case intended to resign his commission in order to devote his time exclusively to searching for the Cocos treasure.

On his return to the island, this time with a partner, he found it invaded by a new influx of treasure hunters. Some were equipped with steam yachts, teams of workmen and mechanical tools. Others were individuals with no assistance beyond their own efforts, determined to enjoy their future wealth entirely alone. Some were prepared to settle for years if necessary, while others hoped for success within a few weeks. All distrusted the others and they would frequently come to blows over a claim before making up their quarrel and setting to work again.

By 1940 it was calculated that more than a hundred people had visited Cocos Island and all of them, without exception, had left again worn and broken men. Many were ruined, for they had put everything they possessed into the search. But although the island had beaten them there was still in their eyes a tiny gleam of the light which had sparked off their great adventure.

"It may be a mistake to look for treasure on the beautiful Pacific and South Sea islands. If pirates were intending to hide it they would be more likely to do so on desolate and inaccessible islands that would prove a deterrent to thieves. . . ."

This was the reasoning of E. F. Knight, a London lawyer who was also the owner of a treasure map. His treasure island was Trinidad, a small strip of land in the South Atlantic eight hundred miles from Rio de Janeiro.

Trinidad is a volcanic block, twisted and ridged by sinister black peaks. The heavy swell that batters her coasts makes landing virtually impossible and there are few attempts made. The Portuguese tried to establish themselves there but soon abandoned the idea, and once an Englishman spent a month there for some secret reason, which Knight knew.

Ever since 1820, treasure from plundered Peruvian churches had been waiting in the heart of the savage island for anyone bold enough to lay hands on it.

Knight did not lack boldness and he possessed all that was necessary for practical purposes. He had a trim, well-found yacht, called the *Alert*, and all that remained was to find partners to share the cost of the expedition. Knight chose nine from the hundred who applied, and set sail.

The *Alert* anchored on November 20, 1889, in the only accessible bay on the south side of the island. The next day two boats were lowered and drove through the surf to the beach. Their occupants set up a camp and began work, but they found the labor backbreakingly hard. They wielded pick and shovel until their muscles were stiff and aching, and shifted tons of earth and gravel in bitterly raw weather. Knight directed operations, map in hand, and was perfectly confident. Their excavations spread until they should have reached the treasure cave and they did ultimately come upon three caves, but all were empty.

Three months after her arrival the *Alert* left the island. Even Knight had given up hope, and the rugged island of Trinidad sank again below the horizon, still guarding its secret.

One day in 1914 the French Minister for Colonial Affairs received the following letter from M. Fawtier, the governor of Tahiti.

There is a rumor at Papeete to the effect that the schooner *Suzanne* has been hired by a group of speculators to hunt for treasure on Pinaki Island. The value of the treasure is estimated at forty-three million francs and it is supposed to consist of valuables from Paraguayan churches, hidden in 1854 by the mutinous crew of the ship carrying them.

We are leaving the South Atlantic with its rolling swell and remote, barbaric islands for the South Seas on whose happy islands a tradition, firmly established by writers such as Bougainville and Pierre Loti, has it that men lead a life free from all worldly troubles.

Yet the gold fever rages even in this tropical paradise. The governor of Tahiti was especially disturbed by the speculators' projected expedition to Pinaki, six hundred miles from Tahiti, because the island belonged to France and the treasure seekers were foreigners. He was concerned to protect France's right to the treasure whose existence

97

had been revealed by one of the mutineers, named Howe, who was planning the expedition in association with some Tahitians. He had no idea how nearly tragic the consequences were to be.

After dispatching his letter to Paris the governor set off on a tour of inspection among the islands. Some days after his departure a clerk came hurrying into the office of the secretary-general who was his temporary deputy.

"The schooner *Suzanne* has already sailed," he said.

The secretary-general felt there was no time to lose. It would be a simple matter for the adventurers to recover the treasure from the lonely atoll in complete security without anyone being the wiser, and without paying France the percentage that was due to her. He thought hard, for he had not yet received instructions from Paris.

"The *Zelée* . . . ?" suggested the clerk.

The *Zelée* was a naval sloop stationed at Tahiti and it would undoubtedly have been in order to send her to Pinaki. Unfortunately she was away on a cruise.

"The *Zelée* doesn't get back for another fortnight," replied the secretary-general. "And by that time it will be too late."

He hunted for an answer to the problem. First he needed a ship. Failing the *Zelée*, he considered using the *Saint Michel*, the postal steamer plying regularly between the islands.

At last he decided to order the *Saint-Michel* to put to sea immediately, but there remained the fact that the steamer had no official status. It would still be necessary to land representatives of the law on Pinaki.

The police, possibly . . . thought the secretary-general.
It was in this way that Fromentin, the chief of police,
and two of his men found themselves delegated to repre-
sent the French government on Pinaki.

The *Saint-Michel* sailed the same evening and three
days later the steamer sighted Pinaki. Fromentin gave a
sigh of relief. The atoll was deserted; there was no sign of
the *Suzanne*.

After putting the three policemen ashore with a tent,
some food and four casks of water, the *Saint-Michel* returned to her postal duties.

Brigadier Fromentin's instructions had been extremely
loosely worded and amounted to no more than being on
the island when the treasure seekers appeared and refusing
them permission to land. It seemed unlikely to be long before they arrived, since the *Suzanne* had sailed some hours
before the *Saint-Michel*.

One fairly important point had been overlooked in these
arrangements, however, and this was how the policemen
were to be taken off the island once their mission was accomplished. It would be awkward for them to board the
transgressing vessel and yet it was clearly impossible to im-
mobilize the *Saint-Michel*, indispensable as she was to the
island's communications. The *Zelée* could not be sum-
moned because she had no radio and was not due in Tahiti
for a fortnight.

At first the policemen did not altogether realize their
situation. In all weathers they kept their guard over the un-
seen treasure and stoically contemplated the horizon, day
after day, without seeing a single ship.

By the end of a week they were growing anxious. They were running short of food and were driven to rationing themselves and attempting to fish in the lagoon, while all the time their water supply grew smaller.

In Tahiti people began by being amused at the plight of the three policemen, indirect sufferers from the treasure hunt. Then amusement turned to anxiety. The comedy threatened to become a tragedy.

Governor Fawtier returned, reprimanded his subordinate and set about finding some way of provisioning the guardians of the atoll. The master of a tramp steamer was sounded but refused to go off his course, arguing that the policemen were in no immediate danger. At the time this was true, but it had been estimated that within a week they would be dangerously short of food.

One remaining hope was that the schooner might be hired on her return to Pinaki, by the governor this time, and sent back at once to the treasure island.

People waited impatiently for her arrival until one evening a sailing ship anchored in the roads of Papeete and with relief they recognized the *Suzanne*'s lines.

"Have you been to Pinaki?" her captain was asked.

"No. We've been looking for copra."

They stared at him in amazement. Had his boat not been hired by a man named Howe to go and hunt for treasure on Pinaki?

"Howe, did you say?" the captain answered. "Yes, he's been in touch with me but nothing has been fixed up yet."

The misunderstanding would have been comic but for the predicament of the three unfortunate policemen left to die of thirst on the island.

The governor, at his wit's end, was about to send the *Suzanne* to the rescue of the men who had been ordered to stop her, when the *Zelée* arrived at Tahiti. Her captain was told he must leave again immediately for Pinaki, but replied that he could not leave before urgent repairs were done to his boiler, for he had only just managed to make Papeete.

The mechanics worked night and day but it was not until March 25 that the sloop dropped anchor off the treasure island. Three blasts on her siren shattered the silence but although a tent could be seen through the glasses there was no sign of life.

A boat was hurriedly lowered and soon sailors leaped out onto the warm sand. In the tent lay the three policemen, too weak to move.

"About time too," croaked Fromentin. "Our water ran out three days ago."

Howe did not abandon his attempt but war intervened before he could put his plans into practice. Careful this time to act within the law, he applied in January 1920 for permission to remove any gold bullion that might be found on Pinaki. He offered the French government a quarter of the value of the treasure, which he estimated at ninety million francs.

The following year the French ambassador in Washington received a similar request from an American, Mark I. Adams, who, more optimistic than Howe, estimated the Pinaki gold to be worth sixty million dollars.

Permission was granted to both Howe and Adams, but Pinaki never gave up its secret. To this day not a single gold bar or a single precious stone has ever been brought back from Pinaki, any more than from the Galápagos, Trinidad, the Marianas, Mauritius or Tristan da Cunha. But as to why it should be so, the islands remain as mysteriously silent as ever.

5

Phantom Islands

THE low-lying bank of gray cloud loomed over the gray miles of sea like an air-borne desert, making of the colorless waste of sky and water a world of unimaginable desolation.

In this emptiness there appeared a small speck like a dark cloud or a flock of migrating birds which mounted higher and grew larger, dispersed in the wind and thickened again and became blacker in the dead light of the astral landscape. Then slowly the stain melted to reveal the masts and funnels of a steamship plowing its slow furrow through the ocean. A Norwegian flag at her stern was wrapped around its pole by the wind.

On the bridge Captain Lars Christiansen stood holding his glasses. His mind was on his strange mission to take possession of an island that had vanished. It was named Dougherty Island after the whaling captain who had discovered it by chance in 1841.

Dougherty had marked the new land's position, estimated its length and entered a detailed description of it in his log: a treeless hill rising to the north with a hollow, snow-filled valley in the center.

On his return to Europe Dougherty informed the Survey Department of his discovery.

They agreed to call it Dougherty Island but told him he was not in fact the island's first discoverer. Dougherty protested that he had seen no mention of it on any charts.

"That may be so," he was told, "but we have records proving that in 1804 seal hunters were based on the island for several weeks. They believed there were actually two islands, but the position of yours leaves no room for doubt."

"Has anyone visited the island within the last forty years?" asked Dougherty.

"No. Seal hunters tried to find it some years later."

"Well?"

"They did not find it."

"There you are then. . . ."

However, the failure of the seal hunters to find the island proved nothing, since for them new land meant, above all else, fresh hunting grounds which it was in their own interest to keep secret to prevent competitors using them in their turn. There was therefore a possibility that, while the discovers could not deny themselves the pleasure of proclaiming their new island's existence, the position they had given for it was a false one, intended to mislead other fishermen.

Eighteen years later, in 1859, the captain of a whaler circled the island and confirmed Dougherty's observations,
as did two seal hunters who stayed there for three days
and reported that many fur-bearing seals made their home
on its shores.

It was this last information that drew two ships to the
island in 1889. Their crews set off with high hopes but returned two months later with discouraging accounts of
their fishing. This was a familiar joke and often covered a
reluctance to reveal exactly where the seals had been
caught.

"Not telling, eh?" the other fishermen chaffed them.

"Look in our hold and see for yourselves."

The hold was barely half full.

The bystanders were taken aback and asked if the seals
had deserted the famous Dougherty Island.

"We've no idea," said the men.

"Isn't that where you've been?"

"Yes, but the island's vanished."

There was a shout of laughter.

"You mean you couldn't find it."

"We can steer a course as well as anyone. We sailed all
around the position marked on the charts and found nothing."

This answer convinced no one, for although the skippers
of seal-hunting ships were excellent seamen, they were
known to rely all too often on their own instinct for navigation rather than on the sextant. It was a method with
few drawbacks when they were returning to well-known
hunting grounds but lacked precision and effectiveness

when it came to finding a tiny island in a wide expanse of empty sea.

The following year other seal hunters made for Dougherty Island. Far from being discouraged by the previous crews' failure, they were secretly glad, for it meant the flocks of seals on the island would not have been thinned.

But the seals were destined to breed safely for another year. The ships never found Dougherty Island. They quartered the area where it was supposed to lie for several days without success. However, as the sky remained overcast throughout their search, the captains could make no reckonings by the sun or stars, and their calculations, based entirely on guesswork, may well have been wrong.

This was the general explanation for the second setback but it reduced the sailor's enthusiasm for the paradise of seals. Four years went by with no mention of Dougherty Island. Then there was a bad season when the seals for some unexplainable reason deserted their usual hunting grounds, and a skipper once more decided to go south and look for the island, hoping to return with his holds packed with sealskins from Dougherty Island.

At the end of the southern winter he returned, well satisfied. Asked if he had found Dougherty Island, he replied that he had found it without the least difficulty.

"I know how to read a chart, that's all," he said.

Certainly the thing seemed simple enough and the captains who had looked for the island unsuccessfully in previous years set sail the next season vowing to make good their disappointment. But when they reached their destination, or rather the point where their destination should have been, they found only empty, wind-swept sea, land-less as far as the eye could see.

For two days the ships combed the ocean that appeared to have risen up and drowned the secret island, then they turned northward again. Their business was to hunt seals, not solve geographical riddles.

When the survey department was told of the vanishing island, they were not greatly impressed. In their view there was no problem, since Dougherty Island had been located and frequently visited. The existence of drawings and de-scriptions of the island, all of which agreed, ruled out the possibility of a bank of mist or a mirage being taken for an island. They maintained the island's disappearance was nothing out of the ordinary and ships failing to find it must simply have committed a navigational error.

Nevertheless many geographers and sailors were not fully satisfied and they awaited further evidence from ships in the area before committing themselves to an opinion. Unfortunately seal hunters, who had no desire to risk an unprofitable voyage in the open sea, were no longer at-tracted by the lure of the mysterious island. As it was not worth equipping a costly expedition simply to determine the position of Dougherty Island, there was nothing for it but to wait until a ship happened to be sailing in that direc-tion.

An occasion was not long in coming. Captain Scott on his way to the Antarctic would pass close to Dougherty Island and he was asked to take photographs of it.

Scott's ship, the *Terra Nova*, reached the exact position

of the island on January 25, 1904. No land was in sight. Scott ordered soundings to be taken and found a depth of over two thousand fathoms, and although the weather was clear the lookout could see no land, not so much as a shadow on the sea on all the wide horizon. Scott concluded the island did not exist and sailed on.

Scott's verdict that the island did not exist seemed to be the death certificate of the celebrated Dougherty Island. Another ship passing through the same latitudes in June 1909 made doubly sure the island had disappeared. This was Shackleton's *Nimrod*, on her way home from the antarctic expedition in the course of which the English explorer had penetrated to within a hundred miles of the South Pole.

Shackleton went to the trouble of looking for the island at two separate points according to the calculations of previous captains, but he saw no sign of land. However, the weather was overcast and he was unable to verify his position by the sun and qualified his findings with the statement that, as researches of the kind were difficult and without stating positively that the island did not exist, he was prepared to say that it was not in the position generally assumed.

Shackleton was less perfunctory than Scott and all he would definitely commit himself to was a miscalculation in the position of Dougherty Island.

"I know the position of Dougherty Island. It's hardly surprising Scott and Shackleton missed it because the reading on the charts is a long way out."

The speaker was a Norwegian whaling captain named Bull, who had come to the British Government with his astonishing claim.

"Have you been there yourself?" he was asked.

"No," replied the captain. "But my information comes from an absolutely reliable source. I have it from the skipper who returned a few years ago with a hold full of skins and seal oil."

"He did not say the charts were inaccurate."

"No, but he told me he'd bet all the tea in China against anyone who contradicted him that, on February 26, 1893, Dougherty Island existed right enough."

"Why did he tell you the exact position?" the captain was asked.

"Because I paid him for the information," was the answer. "The island is crammed with seals and I reckon I can make my own pile out of them."

"You know the island is British territory?"

"Certainly. That's why I've come to ask you for a monopoly, on the understanding that I pay for it."

The British government accepted the offer but had so little faith in Bull's project that they charged a rental of only twenty-five pounds a year.

Bull tried to form a company. All those he approached were shy of the proposition. They were willing enough to invest funds but wanted guarantees, and it was in vain that Bull insisted his ship was bound to make a landfall at Dougherty Island. Still the prospective investors hesitated. Bull redoubled his efforts, holding out promises of fabulous returns, until the start of the 1914–18 war forced him to postpone his plans.

In 1918 Bull resumed his activities but was still unable to take any action. A disappointed man, he kept the secret of Dougherty Island to himself.

Years passed, and when the Norwegian Government was organizing a scientific expedition into the Antarctic Ocean, Bull was asked if he would be willing to reveal the position of Dougherty Island. He refused.

Lars Christiansen, Captain of the *Norvegia*, vowed he would find the island all the same, although he had no more information to go on than his predecessors.

On March 29, 1929, the *Norvegia* lay directly over the position of Dougherty Island as it was marked on the charts. Lars Christiansen stood regarding the long swell that lifted the deck gently beneath his feet. He was certain of his calculations, yet where the island ought to have been there was nothing but the sea.

This meant—but there was no simple answer to what it meant unless he was to deduce that Dougherty Island did not exist when there were sailors who had seen it, described it minutely and made sketches of its appearance.

The theory that the island had vanished in a volcanic eruption was an unlikely one because the regions were known not to be volcanic, and the captain could only return to the old conclusion that there must have been a navigational error on the part of its original discoverers. Christiansen remembered he had been told of another possible location and decided to go and have a look even though Shackleton had found nothing there.

Eight hours later the *Norvegia* cut her engines for the second time while Christiansen checked his position by the sun and then laid down his sextant hopelessly. Once again there was only empty water, furrowed by the antarctic gales all around him.

Impatiently Christiansen gave the signal "full steam ahead" and bore south with hardly an idea where he was going. There may have been a hope in his mind that luck would guide him to the strange island.

The *Norvegia* had been heading south for about fifteen minutes when an officer mounted the bridge and spoke to the captain.

"Sir, I know where to find Dougherty Island."

"What's that?"

The officer repeated, "I've just heard the exact position of Dougherty Island."

Christiansen stared at him coldly. He was in no mood for joking.

"Really. And who told you?"

"Bull."

"You know as well as I do Bull refused to talk before we sailed."

"He's changed his mind. A radio message has just come through. Here—"

Christiansen seized the piece of paper and began feverishly comparing it with his charts. The new reading placed the island a hundred and fifty miles west. He set a fresh course and told the chief to give her everything he had. Suddenly Christiansen was in a frantic hurry as though he were about to discover the island for the first and last time.

The lieutenant told him the reason for Bull's change of heart was that, despairing of ever being able to make use of the hunting grounds himself, he had not felt justified in taking the secret with him when he died, and after the *Norvegia*'s departure had finally made up his mind to tell the island's exact whereabouts.

The *Norvegia* was not a fast ship and it was twenty hours before she arrived at the position given by Bull. At two o'clock in the morning Christiansen gave the engine room "dead slow." They had reached the island, although they could not yet see it through the darkness enclosing sea and sky. Each man aboard peered through the night in the hope of being the first to sight land.

Christiansen had held well off the coast for fear of striking and estimated it to be some two or three miles distant. The crew waited impatiently for daylight to reveal the mysterious island which held all the attraction of something long sought for, even though it should prove nothing but a rocky and inhospitable mass.

At last a gray light crept into the east, wiping out the last stars, and Christiansen snatched up his glasses and scanned the horizon intently. Then bending over his charts he gave the signal to proceed slowly. Another three miles, two miles . . . by now the island should be visible . . . one mile. . . .

It was full daylight and the ocean rolled ahead of them and on either side in long, slow billows. Behind was only water and more water. A pale sun shone through thin cloud, lending the day a gray, unreal quality that resembled the mysterious Dougherty Island itself.

"We'll get our own back," vowed Christiansen. Tracing Dougherty Island was not the *Norvegia*'s only object, for in the same area there were other islands that had been located once beyond all possibility of confusion and then never seen again. Two years after her discomfiture in the matter of Dougherty Island, the *Norvegia* tackled one of these, named Bouvet Island.

Bouvet Island had been discovered on January 1, 1739, by the French navigator Bouvet de Lozier while he was engaged on a search for the Southern continent, Antarctica, and he had at first supposed the island to be an outcrop of the continent itself. He cruised along its coast for ten days, skirting the glacier that gave vent to strange cracks and groans, and the rocks that enclosed it. Then having charted its position Bouvet turned south again.

Cook did not come across Bouvet Island on his voyage in the antarctic seas in 1744, and it seemed that here was a riddle of the same kind later to be presented by Dougherty Island. Fishermen had spoken of a land, good hunting ground for seals, whose position corresponded roughly with that of Bouvet Island, but oddly they claimed to have seen two islands, although disagreeing about the distance separating them.

Lindsay sighted one in 1908, and Morell, in 1822, discovered another which he named Bouvette, after the French explorer. Three years later Norris announced his discovery of two islands which he christened Liverpool and Thompson.

The positions of these islands did not all agree but they were close enough to Bouvet Island to give rise naturally to the assumption that what the Frenchman had sighted was not a single island but one of an archipelago.

In 1893 there was a fresh discovery. An American seal hunter sighted two more islands, still in the same area but, as the sketches he made bore no resemblance to any of the known islands, apparently new.

The problem in this case was not that there was no island in the position indicated but that there were too many.

The inevitable theories were put forward: inaccurate reckonings, willful misrepresentation by seal hunters. Still the sudden proliferation of islands remained a mystery.

In 1898 the German ship *Valdivia* hunted with great thoroughness for all the islands and was only able to discover one, situated some thirty-five miles northwest of the original position of Bouvet Island. The shape of the island seen by the *Valdivia* resembled that of Bouvet Island and this solved part of the mystery, but only part. What had become of the islands of Lindsay, Thompson and Bouvette?

This was the state of affairs when Lars Christiansen set a course for Bouvet Island as it had been charted by the *Valdivia*. Two hours before they were due to sight the island the lookout signaled land ahead.

This must be Lindsay Island, thought Christiansen.

Visibility was good and as the *Norvegia* approached, the shape of the new land was clearly defined against the sky. There was a glacier enclosed by rocks. It was unmistakably Bouvet Island.

"Incredible," said the lieutenant. "According to my calculations we're still twenty miles away." He added that he had checked them several times and was positive of their accuracy.

Christiansen shrugged his shoulders. It looked as though in this part of the world calculations were no longer to be relied on. The continent it fringed had long been an unknown land, a problem fascinating sailors and geographers for three centuries, and the sea itself seemed to have caught some of the mystery that enveloped the Antarctic mainland.

The *Norvegia*'s crew stared at the mass of jagged ice and rock that resembled the drifting wreck of a continent, and indeed the wandering island did seem to be set on some unfathomable course.

"Tomorrow morning it won't be there any more," said a sailor jokingly.

Even this seemed not unlikely in the game played by the islands as they appeared, disappeared and then reappeared in their original positions. Christiansen was not inclined to mount guard on Bouvet Island and all he could do was record its new position and set off again in search of another island.

This time he was pursuing Thompson, whose size and shape allowed no possibility of confusing it with Bouvet Island. Christiansen made a thorough search for it but at the points indicated on his charts he found only empty sea.

About the same time a big Danish five-master, the *Copenhagen*, the greatest sailing ship of her time, was on a voyage from the Argentine to Australia and had also been given the task of locating Thompson Island, which lay directly on her course.

It was never known whether she found it, for the *Copenhagen* vanished in mysterious circumstances. No S.O.S. was ever received from her although several other vessels believed they had seen her running before a storm. Some fishermen from Tristan da Cunha also reported sighting her. But all these observations, made as they were at almost the same time yet in widely separated places, ultimately did no more than deepen the mystery, which was further complicated when a message in a bottle was found stating that the *Copenhagen* had been surrounded and sunk by icebergs in yet another position south of the Cape of Good Hope.

In 1932 a Norwegian whaler was passing Bouvet Island when her skipper's eye was caught by some dark objects being carried slowly toward the island by the sea. He turned off his course to investigate and saw they were fragments of a wreck. One of the timbers bore quite clearly the name *Copenhagen*.

Dougherty, Thompson, Lindsay and Bouvet are not the only phantom islands in the ocean. The Emerald Isle, south of New Zealand, was discovered on December 13, 1821, by Captain Nockells, who described it in great detail, yet in 1909 Shackleton hunted for it in vain.

The Royal Company Islands suffered the same fate. Dumont d'Urville, Shackleton and Mawson in turn failed to find them. The Nimrod archipelago vanished into the mists of the unknown after having been sighted in 1821, as did the island of Aurora and the Jardinos archipelago. Only

Lindsay Island was rediscovered in 1932 by Billow Hansen, skipper of the Norwegian whaler *Sourabaya*.

If there is a practical explanation of the islands' disappearance, which there must be, what is it?

The usual explanations of such phenomena are a huge iceberg or a bank of clouds on the horizon resembling land, or even optical illusions, but none of these possibilities can be admitted in the present cases. These islands were clearly seen, often it was possible to make more sketches of them and, a conclusive proof of their reality, landings were actually made on some of them. But if the initial fact of their existence is not in doubt, how is their disappearance to be explained?

It has already been said that in the ramifications of island hunting navigational errors, either on the part of the original discoverers or of subsequent searchers, have often been suspected, and there is a fair likelihood of such errors occurring. The most famous example is in the case of the Solomon Islands, discovered in 1568 by Alvaro de Mendaña. Twenty-seven years later an expedition set out with the intention of colonizing the new islands but it never found them, and it was not until the end of the eighteenth century that the Solomon Islands were identified for certain.

It has been proved that navigators' errors, especially in reckoning longitude, caused this mistake. But the chronometer had not yet been invented in the time of Alvaro de Mendaña and at the date when the subantarctic islands under discussion were found, seamen had accurate instruments at their command. The only remaining explanation is human fallibility.

Had the islands been victims of submarine earthquakes the tremors must have been on a sufficiently large scale to register on seismographs and would probably have given rise to tidal waves. Moreover the area is not one where such upheavals are common.

Further evidence is that soundings taken at the supposed position of the islands frequently revealed depths of two thousand fathoms or more, much greater than any recorded after submarine disturbances.

If the earthquake theory must be discarded, speculation is forced back to that of confusion with icebergs bearing fragments of rock and soil which fishermen, even on landing, have been able to mistake for islands.

All the same it cannot be hastily concluded that these islands do not exist. It has been seen that Lindsay Island, to cite one example, was rediscovered by chance in latitude 54° S. by 2° 41' E. This discovery taught caution to hydrographers and is the reason why phantom islands are still to be found on many charts.

Volcanic islands are a different problem and do not lead to the same confusion. Their ephemeral nature is well known and nobody takes much notice of their appearances and disappearances.

Such was the case of Sabrina in the Azores, and of Falcon Island in the Pacific Tonga group, which appeared in 1865, was declared a British possession, then disappeared, reappeared and became French, was drowned again and rose in 1900. There was no further sign of it for twenty years until it was sighted by a New Zealand sloop in 1921.

Another vanishing island appeared in 1831 and was claimed simultaneously by Great Britain and the Kingdom of the Two Sicilies. But while diplomats were still arguing the question of its nationality the island disappeared again, only to rise out of the Mediterranean once more thirty years later. This time no power was anxious to claim it.

The *Federation*'s adventure has already introduced another kind of phantom island, the floating islands that are sometimes encountered near the mouths of great rivers in China and around the Amazon.

Yet another kind is brought to mind by the affair of the *Mary Celeste*.

The facts of this story are well known. In 1873 the American brig *Mary Celeste* was found by the bark *Dei Gratia* drifting off the Azores. There was no sign of the crew but the mystery was increased and given an altogether new dimension by the state in which the vessel was found. There were unmistakable signs that she had only recently been abandoned. Clothes were drying on the deck and there were cups of tea still warm in the galley. Yet not one of the ship's boats was missing and there was no explanation of how the crew had disappeared.

Time and again the question was asked and fascinated explorers, historians and storytellers alike. Various solutions of the mystery were put forward and the most reasonable of them, although even this is not wholly satisfying, is that offered by the English writer, Keating, who wrote a book around the affair of the *Mary Celeste*.

His theory was that the brig's crew had been gradually

reduced in the passage between New York and the Azores as a result of brawls, accidents and desertions, until only three men remained aboard, when the *Dei Gratia* encountered the *Mary Celeste*. These three men had come aboard in an irregular manner and were not entered on the ship's roll. The captain of the *Dei Gratia* bought their silence and claimed to have found the brig abandoned in order to be able to claim salvage money.

Other conjectures of varying wildness have been put forward, one of the more interesting being that the ship ran aground on a volcanic island that had risen suddenly in her course. The crew disembarked to inspect the new land, which then disappeared as suddenly as it had come, refloating the *Mary Celeste* while her crew was engulfed with the island and perished.

This theory did not gain much credence, despite the fact that in the Azores, where the *Mary Celeste* was found, such volcanic eruptions are not uncommon. However, a British sailor, Dod Orsborne, claimed to have undergone a similar experience and thought that at the same time he had discovered a clue to the mystery of the *Mary Celeste*.

Dod Orsborne was the hero of some fantastic feats of seamanship, notably that of sailing from England to New Guinea without either maps or compass in a small trawler which he "borrowed" and rechristened the *Girl Pat*. He ran aground one night some eighty miles from the West African coast. At a loss for an explanation, Orsborne waited impatiently for daylight and, in his own words, "in the morning we saw the boat was resting on a sandy island about a mile in circumference and rising about a yard above sea level."

Orsborne also saw another island to the north, and in the early afternoon a third appeared. He was also able to make out the rusty stern of a steamship jutting ten or twelve feet out of the water, the rest of its keel being apparently held fast in another sandbank.

The following night Orsborne succeeded in freeing his boat and when he put into Port Etienne he recounted his strange adventure. He was told that such things had been heard of before and that it was assumed these shifting banks, called by the natives "phantom islands," were formed by submarine currents driving the sand along the sea bed. It collected at the bottom of the sea until it formed actual sandbanks, which were forced gradually to the surface by the pressure of water and remained there sometimes for several days before dispersing.

Dod Orsborne believed the *Mary Celeste* had been a victim of a similar occurrence.

But although Dod Orsborne escaped from his phantom island, it was on an island that he was destined to die. On the morning of December 24, 1957, his body was found in his room in an hotel in Belle-Île, where his ship had put in.

6

Legendary Islands

"GOOD EVENING, Adelantado!"

The old man gently warded off the urchins whose mocking shouts greeted him and sat down, as he did every day, at the end of the mole looking out to sea.

He was known as Pedro de Ulmo. A dozen years earlier the captain of a merchant ship on her way home from Africa had found him clinging to a spar in the sea off the Canaries and brought him to Lisbon.

The castaway could give no clear account of where he came from and when questioned only talked of an "Isle of the Seven Cities" and begged the captain repeatedly to take him back there.

"I can't turn off my course," the captain told him, "but you're bound to find a vessel at Lisbon to take you."

In an undertone he ordered that the poor wretch be locked in a cabin. He had apparently gone out of his mind through his sufferings, for there was no such place as the Isle of the Seven Cities.

In Lisbon Pedro de Ulmo was soon being talked about. The first thing he did was to go to one of the best houses in the city and try to install himself there, claiming it as his own property. It was all the servants could do to drive him away.

Later the same day Ulmo managed to force his way into the Alvarez palace where he requested an interview with the daughter of the house. As soon as she appeared he flung himself on his knees in front of her, swearing that he had not forgotten her, and still loved her and wished to marry her as soon as possible. The girl was terrified of the ruffianly character declaring passionate love for her and promptly had him thrown out, threatening to call the police if he came back.

The next day it was the turn of a government official to receive a visit from Ulmo.

"I have come to give an account of my mission from the king," he announced.

"Has the king given you a mission?" asked the astonished official.

"I was to discover the Isle of the Seven Cities and I am happy to say that this has been accomplished. My ship was wrecked and all my companions perished, but I have returned to give His Majesty full account of my discoveries."

"I don't know what you're talking about," answered the official coldly. "Send in a report if you like and I will see it is put into the proper hands."

And he showed his visitor out.

The following week Pedro de Ulmo presented himself again, asking for an audience with the king. He was put off with vague promises but when a letter arrived a few days later, again mentioning the Isle of the Seven Cities, someone undertook to look up the expedition in the archives. He finally unearthed a contract, made in 1490, between João II and a certain Pedro de Ulmo who was to set off in search of new lands. Ulmo engaged himself to take possession of them in the name of Portugal and in return was to be called *adelantado* or governor. The file held nothing besides the contract and that had been signed a hundred years before.

This time there could be no doubt the castaway was mad as he claimed to be the reincarnation of Pedro de Ulmo, who had presumably been lost at sea, since no news had ever been heard of his expedition. To get rid of him they showed him the contract.

"If you were really Pedro de Ulmo," they told him, "you would be more than a hundred years old by now. Now go away and don't be a nuisance."

The story of Pedro de Ulmo spread through Lisbon. People told how he had gone back to the Alvarez palace and insisted he was to be married to a lady whose portrait hung on the wall of the room where he was received. The portrait was that of the great-grandmother of the girl who had already sent the so-called Pedro de Ulmo away.

If the queer castaway was mad, it seemed there was at least a sort of logic in his madness. He claimed to be Pedro de Ulmo who had sailed under the reign of João II to find an island in the Atlantic where, according to tradition, some Catholics had fled in the eighth century to escape the Moorish invasion. Before his departure this Pedro de Ulmo had in fact been betrothed to Seraphita Alvarez, the great grandmother of the girl to whom the castaway had declared his love.

Everything was as though this were the real Pedro de Ulmo come back from the dead, more than a century after his expedition.

The general opinion was that the man was either an impostor or some poor wretch who had lost his reason after a shipwreck and, knowing the story, imagined he was Pedro de Ulmo.

Far from being deterred by the disbelief he encountered, the castaway tried again and again to persuade shipowners to provide him with a vessel to find his fabulous island again, but they all sent him away. At last he took ship for the Canaries and tried again at Las Palmas to interest someone in his project.

He expected to be asked questions and told to bring proof of his story, but hardly had he uttered the name of his island than people said calmly:

"Oh yes, the Isle of the Seven Cities. That's its legendary name. Its real name is Barodon Island. So you've been there too, have you?"

Amazed at hearing someone who knew of his island, the castaway cried: "You know it! It is real!"

"Of course it's real. In fine weather you can even see it from one of the Canary Islands, the Île de Fer."

"I knew it. I knew it was true," said the castaway with tears in his eyes.

"You're not the first claiming to have landed there. But as for going back—"

"Won't you let me have a boat?"

"I'm telling you, you're not the only one who's discovered Barodon Island, or the first to claim possession of it, but they say Barodon's a place you can only see once in a lifetime. So you see in that case if we lent you a ship . . ."

The castaway was frantic. He knocked on every door insisting he was the *adelantado* of the Isle of the Seven Cities, but people only listened to him kindly and sent him away.

He developed a habit of going to the port of Las Palmas every day, always to the same spot on the mole, and staring at the horizon in the direction of his island. He no longer pestered captains to take him there. He would stand, motionless, his eyes full of private visions, seeming to live outside time. Transformed by his legend, he had become a legendary figure himself. He was Pedro de Ulmo.

Fishermen found Pedro de Ulmo one morning on the quay, his face turned toward the sea and his eyes wide open, with a strange, intent stare. His flesh was as cold as though he were carved out of stone.

The island madness killed Pedro de Ulmo but the island that destroyed him existed in the no man's land between the imaginary and the real. Barodon Island is a mystery but for two centuries it was marked on the charts.

When Emanuel of Portugal, the same king who received Fernão Lopes, the hermit of Ascension Island, renounced his claim to the Canary Islands in 1519, he included an eighth island in the group. This was the celebrated island where Pedro de Ulmo claimed to have landed and which was known as the undiscovered or the lost island.

Two Spaniards hunted for it unsuccessfully in 1526 and their failure seemed the more surprising in the light of a report received by a judge of the royal court in the Canaries on April 3, 1570. This came from the governor of the Île de Fer and announced that the contours of the island had been clearly seen by more than a hundred witnesses forty leagues to the northwest.

The Portuguese pilot Pero Velho in his turn said he had landed on Barodon during a storm and found there a spring of fresh water, some tracks and the remains of a camp. The Spaniard Marco Verde also related how he had gone ashore for a few hours on a similar island in the same area.

Navigators and geographers assumed the island's existence to be beyond doubt but other expeditions between 1604 and 1721, all of them under the command of experienced seamen such as Villalobos, Perez de Acosta, and Gaspar Dominguez, saw nothing but empty sea.

Meanwhile Barodon was being seen so clearly from the Île de Fer that it was even possible to make sketches of what it looked like.

The elusive island had to have a legend and it soon became identified with St. Brendan's island, of which the name Barodon is a corruption. Brendan was an Irish bishop of the sixth century who set sail to look for an island of the blest which, the chronicle says, he at last discovered, although only after several false starts. Once, it is recorded, he disembarked by mistake on the back of a gigantic whale which he took for an island.

People believed from the story of St. Brendan that the Island of the Blest lay somewhere in the region of the Canaries and was in fact the phantom island that could be seen from the Île de Fer.

The mysterious island continued to appear and could be seen to consist of two round hills separated by a deep valley, filled on some days by a white flock of clouds. Numerous bays and rocky crags were visible, all very distant but perfectly clear.

Sketches of Barodon Island went from hand to hand until a certain pilot happened to see one. He stared at it intently for a moment, then said he had seen it before.

"Very possibly," he was told. "From the Île de Fer like hundreds of other people."

He replied that he had never been near the Île de Fer.

"Off the coast of Madeira?"

"No. All my voyages have been in the south, along the African coast."

"No one has ever seen Barodon off the coast of Africa," people said positively.

"I didn't say I saw it off the coast of Africa." He thought a moment. "It wasn't in Portuguese waters, either. More to the west, I think."

Again the pilot stared at the sketch in his hand.

"I know I've seen this more than once, quite frequently in fact."

"You'll be the only one."

Suddenly his face cleared.

"I don't think I am the only one. This is another of the Canary Islands. Palma."

"But Palma is much farther north."

The pilot insisted the sketch showed at least the upper portion of the western approach to Palma.

Geographers studied the sketches and seamen took bearings until they came to the conclusion that the pilot was right. Barodon Island was simply a mirage, a reflection of Palma given back off the clouds in certain atmospheric conditions.

As for the explorers who claimed to have landed there, they were telling the truth but they had landed on the island of Madeira.

Pedro de Ulmo's adventure takes us into the very heart of island legends. Islands are essentially mysterious. The sea at once isolates them and opens out an infinite number of horizons, and primitive minds have quite naturally peopled these strange lands, lost in uncharted oceans, with even stranger beings. In legend they are the dwellings of the dead as well as of the immortals, of the damned as well as of the blest, and of all the fabulous creatures whose existence lies somewhere on the edge of human reason.

The poet Pindar speaks of a realm of Saturn in the midst of the ocean, the home of "all those whose souls have dwelt three times on earth and three times in Hades and are pure of all injustice." Hesiod fixes the last resting place of heroes on the same island and all ancient mythologies agree in setting their paradise on an island, since islands are places especially singled out by spirits. Among these islands are Helvoetsfuis at the mouth of the River Maas, Boyard in the Baltic, and Onogorojima in the Sea of Japan.

Devil's islands are fewer, the best known being the Scandinavian island of Hornum which is haunted by the ghosts of thieves, murderers and castaways.

These islands of the dead, whether they are the dwellings of the blest or the damned, are not invariably the creations of myth. Tombs and tumuli have been found in the Gulf of Morbihan off the coast of Brittany, off the Dalmatian coast, in the North Sea, in the New Hebrides, the Caroline Islands, and of course on Easter Island.

But the dead are not the only inhabitants of these legendary islands. Often they are the realm of monsters, like êl Ramany, which the Arabs believed is peopled by dwarfs, and Wak where queer "woman trees" grow, from whose branches the bodies of women hang by their hair.

These islands are often inhabited by women who symbolize their seductive qualities and also serve as reminder of the island peoples whose easy moral code first attracted the early navigators to the Pacific. Such are the Arab Geziret el Nessa, the Greek Lemnos, and the "land of immortal girls" in the South Seas northwest of Fiji. Among western islands in the Middle Ages was the great island of women, sought in vain by sailors, and all the many lands which, as one chronicler puts it, "have been visited in other times and inscribed in the map, yet none knows whether they are fairy islands or have melted away."

Melted away like poor Pedro de Ulmo's island of the Seven Cities or like the mythical Antilia, with which it was sometimes confused.

Close to Antilia lay another island, perhaps the only one navigators did not attempt to explore, where an enormous hand was said to rise out of the sea and drag people to the bottom.

Yet it is the attraction of such enchanted islands that has led explorers all over the world. Slowly but surely in the wake of their ships the shapes of imaginary islands were swept away and out of the night of legend emerged fresh, sunlit isles, solid enough and their positions carefully charted, yet still preserving like a halo something of the mystery that is their birthright.

7

Pirates of the Islands

"HAVING been found guilty of piracy the prisoners, Joseph and Alexander Rorique, are hereby condemned to death."

December 8, 1893. The lamps did nothing to cheer the dim, rainy twilight that filtered through the high windows of the Maritime Court at Brest. The dreadful sentence, which the court heard standing, spelled the end of a story that had begun two years earlier, almost to the day, under the blue skies of the South Seas and reached its climax in the fog and drizzle of the Breton port.

No one moved but all eyes were turned to the empty dock. There was nothing unusual in this, for in the Maritime Court the accused were not present when the sentence was pronounced. But on this occasion the custom had an especial significance, since the case of the Rorique brothers was doubly strange. Not only had there been no conclusive proof of their guilt, but even their real identity was unknown.

A few moments later two men, Joseph and Alexander Rorique, aged about thirty-five and forty, with a certain nobility of face and bearing, stood pale-faced in the dock and learned they had only a few more days to live.

Alexander was the first to recover himself. "We must not give way," he urged his brother. "One day God will judge these men as they have judged us." Then, with linked arms, they returned to their cell.

On December 15, 1891, a trim schooner, the *Niurahiti*, glided through the calm waters of Papeete roads. She belonged to Hinoï Pomaré, a Polynesian prince who traded cheerfully among the French South Sea islands. Among the nine men aboard her were Gibson, the supercargo, and his deputy whose name was entered on the roll as Joseph Rorique.

The *Niurahiti* was bound for the Tuamotu archipelago, but she was destined never to reach it. She was seen ten days later at Kaukura where a Frenchman, Alexander Rorique, Joseph's brother, went aboard, but Prince Hinoï waited in vain for further news of her.

At first he did not worry unduly, thinking that perhaps her master had turned off his course to pick up a particularly valuable cargo, for the schooner's movements were not fixed to a strict timetable like those of ships belonging to big companies. In these regions where the hurry of Western life was unknown a certain amount of freedom was left to the individual. But early in March Hinoï did send another vessel in search of his ship. It called at various islands where the crew questioned inhabitants and sailors and it returned to Tahiti with disquieting news. The *Niurahiti* had vanished, and Hinoï could only conclude she must have struck a reef and sunk.

At the very moment when Hinoï was mourning his lost schooner, a half-caste came to the naval authorities in the Philippines with a curious tale. He claimed to have important information regarding a case of piracy, but his appearance was so disreputable they refused to listen to him. However, when he returned the next day they agreed for the sake of peace to hear what he had to say.

He told them his name was Mirey and he was cook aboard the sailing ship *Poi Avarua*.

"The one owned by a Frenchman and a Canadian called Georges de Vernier and Louis Toussaint?" asked the authorities.

Mirey agreed, but claimed the men's real name was Rorique and they were brothers. He said the ship was in fact the *Niurahiti* belonging to Prince Hinoï of Tahiti, but the brothers had changed her name and rid themselves of the Polynesian crew. He himself had saved his life only by swearing secrecy.

Mirey's story was listened to skeptically by the Spanish authorities, who were more inclined to believe the cook was bent on some private vengeance. All the same, they sent an officer aboard the ship with instructions to examine her papers.

They had anticipated no more than a simple formality but Vernier and Toussaint were unable to produce any papers and underneath the name of the vessel, which had been freshly painted, another name was still decipherable— *Niurahiti.*

Vernier and Toussaint vigorously protested their innocence and abused Mirey so roundly that he sought the protection of the Spanish militia. Eventually the governor resolved to send all three men to Manila in custody and put the matter in the hands of the French consul, whose province it really was. He could judge the affair himself.

The consul in Manila obtained two significant admissions at the start of his inquiries. Firstly, Vernier and Toussaint admitted their names were Alexander and Joseph Rorique and, secondly, that they had annexed the schooner for their own purposes, although intending to return it to Prince Hinoï. Asked what became of her crew, they said they had either died of illness or accidents or had deserted.

"They are lying," Mirey insisted. "The Roriques killed them. I saw the murders with my own eyes."

Mirey described what had happened, occasionally pausing but able to supply plenty of detail when it was asked for.

At ten o'clock on the evening of the fourth of January Mirey and Gibson, the supercargo, were dozing in the cabin, overcome by the heat. There was no wind and even the sound of water lapping against the prow seemed to have dropped to nothing. The ship was becalmed in a smooth, oily sea.

They lay tossing on their bunks until suddenly two loud bangs brought them both to their feet. For a moment they thought they had been dreaming, since there was no further sound, and the same stifling silence enfolded them again. At length Gibson climbed up on deck, with Mirey behind him.

Under a hard coppery sky the figure of Alexander Rorique, feet slightly apart and quite still, stood impassively beside the wheel. At his feet a man lay face down in a pool of blood. Gibson recognized the thick lips and crinkly hair of the captain, Téhahé.

The supercargo made a dive at Rorique but fell heavily onto the deck with two bullets in his chest. Almost at once Joseph Rorique sprang from a hatchway and levered the body over the side.

"As for you," he threatened Mirey, who stood trembling with only his head showing above the companion ladder. "If you come any nearer I'll kill you."

Mirey tumbled hastily back to rejoin the rest of the crew below.

The hand of death was on the *Niurahiti* and was never to release her. The next morning Mirey's inquisitive goatee again appeared through the hatchway.

"What is it now?" asked Alexander Rorique.

A Polynesian passenger was complaining of violent pains in the stomach. Alexander promised to mix him some medicine and gave the sick man a bowl of water with some white powder stirred into it. An hour later the man died, foaming at the mouth.

"What is it to do with you?" Joseph said roughly to Mirey and the seamen. "The poor devil had a contagious disease and there was nothing we could do for him. Now help me sling the body overboard and stay on deck and work for your living. I'm not going to feed idle mouths."

The men obeyed the Roriques as though they were the incarnation of all the wicked spirits who ever sought men's death and damnation.

However, nothing happened in the next few days and the *Niurahiti* continued her voyage, although Mirey noticed she kept well away from land and seemed to avoid contact with other ships. He himself did not share the crew's fear of the Roriques, knowing they were no devils but simple thieves who had stolen the ship and would not hesitate if necessary to rid themselves of tiresome witnesses.

One morning a heavy sea was running and Alexander called all hands on deck to shorten sail. He had been cursing the crew's laziness when he suddenly changed his tone and, producing a bottle of rum, said quite pleasantly, "Here, you idle good-for-nothings, get this inside you. You could do with a little pick-me-up."

Two of them took the quart bottle he held out to them but the others hung back. Alexander laughed.

"So you don't want it? The more fool I to give it to you."

An hour later there were screams of fear from below.

"Go and see what's up," Joseph told Mirey, who was preparing a meal.

Sensing that one more disaster had struck the *Niurahiti*,

the cook could hardly force his trembling limbs down the ladder. Entering the cabin he saw two figures writhing on the deck and recognized the two seamen who had drunk the rum.

"We were afraid this would happen," commented the brothers without emotion. "The passenger's illness was contagious. There's nothing we can do for them."

A few minutes later the men stiffened in their last convulsions.

"What a ship," sighed the brothers. "We'll have to do all the work ourselves if the two devils we have left are too bone idle to move."

But it was terror, not idleness, that paralyzed the two remaining seamen, the terrible fear of dying as suddenly and horribly as their fellows. They almost refused to eat for fear of being poisoned and would only nibble a few bananas. Their behavior only irritated the already bad tempers of the brothers, until one day, when they had been ordered to set the flying jib, Alexander was infuriated by their clumsiness into drawing his pistol and firing a few shots into the air.

The shots were followed by the sound of two splashes as the seamen flung themselves into the water, convinced they were being murdered. Joseph Rorique gave a quick turn to the wheel and the two figures were left struggling in the *Niurahiti*'s wake. It was the end of the schooner's crew.

"He's lying," protested the brothers when they had heard Mirey's story.

"Ah yes?" said the consul softly. "Then I should be interested to hear how you explain the disappearance of the crew."

"Willingly," answered Alexander, and he told his story.

The scene was once again the deck of the schooner. It was January 5th, and the time was eight o'clock. The night was oppressively hot and still, and Alexander Rorique was standing by the wheel. At Gibson's request he had taken over the command of the ship, replacing Téhahé, the captain, who was ill and unable to take his watch. The truth was that Gibson had seized the opportunity to demote Téhahé, whom he considered incompetent, and put Alexander Rorique, a thoroughly experienced seaman, in his place. Rorique said he had agreed to this under the impression that Gibson was the vessel's owner.

Téhahé came on deck to call the seamen to their evening prayers and Alexander told them to move farther off because his brother was sick. They retired grumbling to the stern but dispersed without trouble when their prayers were finished.

An hour later Alexander saw that Maneiki, the helmsman, was asleep. Cursing he picked up a swab and angrily clouted the man across the face, whereupon Maneiki woke with a start and ran screaming to tell his fellow seamen the white man had tried to kill him. Seeing the whole crowd of them advancing on him armed with belaying pins, Alexander drew his pistol and fired it into the air. Téhahé then screamed something at his men, drew his own pistol and fired.

Alexander flung himself to one side to avoid the shot and

then leaped at Téhahé. Realizing the game was up, since the white man was both taller and more powerfully built than himself, the captain retreated in terror. He had only one shot left in his pistol and suddenly lost his head and dived headlong into the sea and swam away.

Gibson had not interfered in the ridiculous affray, but seeing Téhahé dive overboard and knowing he faced certain death unless rescued at once, he climbed onto the poop to try to throw him a line.

The *Niurahiti* was totally out of control at this moment, for although the seamen were crowded into the stern not one of them had sufficient presence of mind to take the wheel, and veering in a sudden gust of wind, the ship went about of her own accord. Gibson's voice could be heard in the darkness calling Téhahé when a sudden dry, splintering sound filled the air, followed by a heavy thud on the deck and the sound of a splash. The mainsail tackle had broken loose and struck the unfortunate Gibson, hurling him into the water.

Alexander hesitated. His brother was sick and he knew if he left the ship with a boat to look for the two men the crew would mutiny completely. He was powerless to do more than shout and search the black water with the flickering light of a torch. For an hour the *Niurahiti* circled the scene of the tragedy; then, as nothing was to be seen, she continued her course.

Three days later, on the morning of the 7th, one of the seamen came to tell the brothers their passenger had died. Alexander went below but could only confirm that the man was dead. At midday he had the corpse buried at sea.

From then on the seamen, already shattered by the loss of Téhahé and Gibson, were a prey to fear and superstition. Alexander told them to pull themselves together and offered them the rum. Two of the men refused it but the friendly gesture seemed to reassure them all.

The following night the shadowy outline of an island showed above the horizon.

"We'll have to go about," Joseph told Mirey, who was on deck. "Go and wake the men."

Mirey went below and returned almost at once.

"Well?"

"There's no one there."

Joseph cursed and asked himself what fresh tricks the damned seamen were up to. He found it was no trick. The men had deserted. They must have swum away from the ship and reached the island.

"I'm not going to waste my time looking for them," growled Alexander.

They were in the region of the Gilbert Islands when he decided to run for Peru, where he hoped to replenish his crew before continuing his voyage and then returning to Tahiti.

"And that is exactly what happened," finished Alexander.

The French consul at Manila considered the two stories, Mirey's and Alexander's. Either of them could be true, but there were no witnesses and no proof to decide between them. The accuser, Mirey, was an unreliable character, perfectly capable of lying to serve his own ends, but neither was the available information concerning the Rorique brothers particularly reassuring.

They had first been seen in the South Seas about 1888 in command of a cutter. They were vague about where it had come from and it was in all likelihood stolen. They were next heard of in Sydney aboard a bark, the *Vagabond*, when they were involved in a case of poisoning. They left her at Tahiti, and were later known to be running a ship chandler's and a small trade in mother-of-pearl.

The consul washed his hands of the affair. Pirates or no, it did not rest with him but with the Maritime Court at Brest to pass judgment on the Roriques, and he resolved to send them to France at the earliest opportunity, and Mirey with them.

He asked for a ship to transport the prisoners, but it was not until March 7, 1893, that they were taken aboard a ship for Saigon. They remained shut up in irons for fifteen days without fresh air before being transferred to the *Shamrock*, which was to take them to France.

The journey was a terrible experience. Joseph recalled, "We were continually in irons and unable even to lie down at full length. We suffered all that men can possibly endure and I would be crucified a dozen times over rather than live through such fearful days again. Even now I tremble with anger and disgust to think what we endured."

On April 24th the *Shamrock* anchored in the roads of Toulon. The brothers emerged pale and wasted and almost blinded by the sunlight they had not seen for so many weeks, but their sufferings were not yet over. There was still the long train journey to be endured before they reached Brest, during which people came and stared curiously at them in the railway stations and abused them without even knowing their crime. They reached Brest on April 27th and their examination began.

The case was presented in the following terms: The crew of the schooner *Niurahiti* having disappeared completely with the exception of three persons, these three were all equally involved. The first two, the Rorique brothers, maintained the men had died as a result of illness or accident or had deserted. The third, the cook Mirey, swore the Roriques were responsible for the majority of their deaths.

One thing weighed heavily against the Roriques and this was their unquestionably having taken possession of the schooner. They admitted having changed her name and falsified her papers, facts which it was scarcely possible to deny, and even assuming they were sincere in their declared intention of returning the vessel to Prince Hinoï Pomaré they had, in borrowing the schooner, a clear-cut motive for murder.

The judges were faced with a difficult decision and to make it they had to ask themselves two questions. Which of the stories was the true one, and which side was the more trustworthy, Mirey or the Roriques?

Admittedly acceptance of the Roriques' story involved an astonishing number of coincidences. It was necessary to believe in the crew mutinying simply as the result of a blow with a swab administered to a lazy sailor; in the captain's panic that led him to jump overboard; in the extraor-

dinary accident leading to Gibson's death; in the coinciden-
tal death of the passenger; and finally in the crew's sudden
desertion. Mirey's story, on the other hand, was plausible
enough if one accepted the initial fact that the Roriques intended to steal the ship. Such a sequence of killings would
then be a logical part of their behavior.

There was one considerable flaw in the cook's argument,
a flaw that threatened to destroy the whole structure of his
story, and this was his own existence, the very fact that he
was alive, to accuse the Rorique brothers at all. He said
they had spared his life in return for a promise to keep silence, when it was obvious the brothers would have no
guarantee such a promise would be kept. It seemed possible that the man now accusing them might originally have
been an accomplice who later wished to put himself in
the right by denouncing the brothers to the police.

In the long run both stories seemed to contain much the
same proportions of truth and falsehood and there seemed
no more reason for accepting one than the other. There
was apparently more to be gained from comparing the
characters of the three men concerned and exploring the
almost equally insoluble problem of who was Mirey and
who were the Rorique brothers.

Mirey was a mulatto, born in Tahiti, and the most defi-
nite piece of information to be obtained about his past was
that he had twice been convicted and imprisoned, once for
a year, the second time for six months, for stealing and re-
ceiving stolen goods. During the trial Mirey also admitted
giving his wife to a Chinese in payment of his debts.

If he was lying the motive for his accusation could be

found in revenge, for the Roriques had several times beaten him for thieving.

Mirey's character, then, was hardly one to inspire confidence, but were those of the Roriques any better?

This in the last resort was the issue before the court. The two brothers seemed perfectly willing to state their identity. Joseph Rorique, born December 6, 1865, at Natal. Alexander Rorique, born August 2, 1856, at Pretoria. Profession: sailor.

"What nationality was your father?"

"I imagine he was French, since the name is French," answered Alexander. "He died before I was eleven. My mother's name was also French."

"Where did you go to school?"

"In Natal, where my parents lived."

The questions went on but all received the same evasive answers. Alexander gave the names of some ships he had sailed on but that was all.

"They're lying," was the opinion of the court. "Is Rorique even their real name?"

The French consul in the Transvaal was requested to make inquiries about them. He could find no trace of the prisoners' identity at Pretoria but said the town's records were in chaos.

One reason for the court's insistence on the Roriques' identity was a suspicion held from the outset that the pirates might be convicts who had escaped from Noumea. During their stay in Tahiti they had said very little of their origins. People knew vaguely they had come from Australia but that was all. There was an air of mystery surrounding them which their judges could only suppose to be one of crime, and they were so sure of this that the brothers were condemned to death after a hearing, often extremely lively, but in which strict impartiality was not always preserved.

The brothers had a walk of several hundred yards back to their prison after each session of the court and the local inhabitants formed the habit of collecting to watch them. The quiet dignity of their bearing after their sentence so impressed the crowd that instead of hurling insults at them as on earlier days, they came close to encouraging and comforting them. People stared curiously at their strange clothes, which had been noted by all the local newspapermen, their white trousers, canvas shoes and straw hats.

One day as the brothers, with their police escort, were passing the local laundry an old woman with a wrinkled, tear-stained face approached Alexander. He turned to look at her and his expression changed. Seeing she was about to speak he stopped and put a hand on his lips for silence, then walked on.

None of those present understood the meaning of the scene, which lasted only a few seconds, but the simple, wordless exchange was to throw light on a dark and tragic affair.

A few days after this the president of the court received a large envelope which he found, on opening, to contain a sheet of paper folded in four on which were a few lines of writing.

The Rorique brothers' real names are Eugène and Léonce de G——. They belong to an ancient Belgian family and have always led an honorable life. They have been decorated for rescues at sea.

The letter was not signed but it was later found to have been written by the old woman at the laundry, who had formerly been in the service of the de G—— family in Belgium.

After this, letters, signed and unsigned, flowed in bringing detailed information and illumination about the lives of the Roriques. Inquiries were set on foot and soon proved that Alexander and Joseph Rorique really were Léonce and Eugène de G——.

> We have no crimes to hide [wrote Léonce in a letter to the president of the court, admitting his real identity], but we have an unhappy family, a poor mother especially, whose name we did not wish to dishonor by dragging it before the courts. We were aware the mystery surrounding the name Rorique would weigh against us and we knew too that if I were to appear before the court as Léonce de G——, wearing the Belgian Cross, a Norwegian gold medal and three more Belgian decorations, all awarded for courage and devotion, and my brother Eugène were to appear wearing the same cross, earned when he was only nineteen years old, and his Norwegian gold medal, then the judges would believe our story. If we had done this the prosecution would not have treated us as pirates and escaped convicts. But we preferred to lose our honor and even our lives under an assumed name than cause the least anxiety to the poor mother we love so dearly.

The Belgian government confirmed that Léonce and Eugène de G—— had rescued the crews of two Norwegian barks with outstanding heroism, within the space of ten months.

Eugène and Léonce de G—— belonged to a wealthy family but from childhood it had been their ambition to go to sea. The sea cast her spell over them as over so many others. They traveled to England with the object of gaining commissions in the British merchant marine and, as a precaution against any difficulties that might result from their foreign nationality, they adopted the more British-sounding pseudonym Rorick, in place of their own name.

From the moment they adopted their new name they seemed to take on a new personality with it, and perhaps here lies the heart of what deserves to be called the mystery of the Rorique brothers, and the reason why these wealthy young men with the prospect of honorable careers in the marine before them should have suddenly become adventurers. The strange metamorphosis that made of them possible pirates and murderers came to them through the call of the islands, and their fate was bound up in the mystery enfolding the islands of the South Seas.

Knowledge of the brothers' true identity still did not solve the problem of their guilt or innocence, although it may well be imagined that the judges would have felt more sympathy for the de G—— brothers than for the unknown Roriques and the trial might have gone a quite different way. Unfortunately sentence had already been passed and no fresh evidence could be brought to secure a reversal, although when the prisoners' antecedents were taken into consideration the sentence was commuted to life imprisonment.

Feeling continued to run high concerning what many people were now openly referring to as a miscarriage of justice. Clemenceau wrote furiously in *Justice*: "The two Roriques still languish on the Île d'Oléron. What is to be done about it? Pardon is no solution, for if they are guilty why should they be pardoned, and if they are innocent how can they be left to bear the stain of an infamous crime?"

In Belgium committees were formed to work for the Roriques' pardon, since they had rapidly attained the stature of heroes, and martyrs to filial piety. The president was inundated with requests for a pardon, among them from time to time a letter edged with plain black: Madame de G——.

Still there was no pardon and in its place people began to call for a retrial.

There was a moment when this seemed almost possible. In July 1894 a letter arrived from Manila written by some men who had been Mirey's fellow prisoners when he was awaiting transport to France with the Roriques. According to his fellow prisoners Mirey had been agitated about the penalties he was liable to incur if he should withdraw his accusation against the Roriques. This was taken as evidence that Mirey in fact had been lying, sufficiently strong to warrant a re-examination of the case and a fresh trial.

Still the petitions rolled in. In the *Journal* Séverine started a campaign, in which he was followed by the entire

Belgian press, demanding: "Stop this judicial scandal! These two poor souls have suffered too much. . . ."

The magistrates argued against reopening the case on the grounds that the Manila letter, being signed by persons who had themselves been in prison at the time and therefore suspect, did not constitute fresh evidence. It was no longer possible to prove their assertions and Mirey, now that he was out of danger, would obviously admit nothing. Moreover he could not be indicted for false witness as at the trial he had been called as an accessory, not as a witness.

Matters reached a standstill. Even supposing Mirey to have been lying, it was possible he had done so to clear himself of the charge of complicity and his lies did not imply the brothers' innocence.

At this stage only a pardon could have saved the brothers, but still it did not come. There was no decision and the campaigns continued until 1898, when they stopped suddenly. Léonce de G—— had died in prison.

His death silenced the brothers' most bitter enemies and Eugène received a pardon.

When he landed at Anvers he was received like a martyr. Fetes were held in his honor but these marks of affection seemed painful to him. He left Belgium, married a French girl and went to live in Paris, where Séverine, Jaques Dhur, Simone, Gémier and Loïe Fuller were among his friends. But he quickly tired of sympathy that was perhaps no more than curiosity. He was dedicated to a life of travel and adventure and was powerless to break free from the tragic clouds that surrounded him.

He was for a time in the service of the Prince of Monaco and left that to go to Central America. In 1926 he was police chief of the port of Trinidad, a strange reversal for the onetime convict, but he was not suited to the job and began planning to go prospecting for diamonds in Colombia. Then, changing his mind, he turned up as consul for Costa Rica in New Orleans.

But he was not made for a fixed and sedentary life. In 1929 he was in Colombia and it was there that fate dealt him her last blow. One day police came to arrest him. The former police chief of Trinidad was accused of stealing a briefcase from an American traveler.

Eugène protested his innocence as he had done once before in the Maritime court at Brest. A few days later his body was found in the cell where he had been confined. The exact circumstances of his death were never known. His life was destined to be shrouded in mystery to the end.

8

The Island of New France

"TERRE *aimée avant que connue*
Nouvelle France, pays d'or . . ."

The last lights of Europe twinkled in the fading night
and Antoine Lurin leaned over the side of the three-master
Chandernagor watching the glow of the Flemish port of
Flushing, and feeling a movement of panic inside him now
that he was on the brink of adventure. "Beloved country
. . . golden land. . . ." He, like all the other passengers
aboard, had sung the simple hymn as the ship weighed
anchor, but now his enthusiasm fell and the golden land
toward which he was bound, this island of New Britain
which was to be the cradle of a new France, disturbed
more than it attracted him.

Lurin looked at the men, women and children crammed into the steerage space who were to share his strange adventure. It was an adventure that had begun two years earlier, one day in July 1877, in the most prosaic way possible, in the personal column of a newspaper. FREE COLONY OF PORT-BRETON. LAND FOR SALE, FIVE FRANCS THE HECTARE. MAKE YOUR FORTUNE.

The offer was tempting and Lurin wrote. A week later a reply came from Marseilles explaining that the free colony of Port-Breton was situated on one of the Melanesian Islands between the Solomon Islands and New Guinea. The land was fertile and productive, particularly suitable for the cultivation of cotton and sugar cane. The first shipful of colonists would be sailing shortly.

The colonies had always appealed to Lurin and here was an opportunity for him too to set sail for the wonderful island. He wrote again and was sent a contract to the effect that: "The colony shall supply a house, built according to the manner of the country, either in a village, by the seashore or on a road, together with such land as I have paid for. Beyond this I undertake to support myself and my family by my own efforts and industry."

At the moment when Antoine Lurin was turning the prospectus for New France over in his hands, a tall man with a loud, passionate voice and a commanding presence was addressing an attentive audience in a public hall in Marseilles on the same subject. He was approaching his peroration: "The idea of our colony is born of religious and patriotic feelings—" Here he fixed his eagle eye on a priest in the front row, lifted his arms to heaven and, stressing every syllable, intoned, "Europe is being torn asunder, the clouds are gathering on the horizon, there is continual strife and in the innermost depths of our hearts, as we are good Catholics and Frenchmen, we cannot hide it from ourselves. Alas, poor country, where is your glory now? Eldest child of the Church, where is your crown?"

Carried away by his own eloquence, he explained that this colony was to be an asylum for the homeless, a home for the persecuted, for good Christians who could not live under the secular laws of republican France, and for all those who wished to lead a free and honorable life. For all these he, Charles Marie Bonaventure du Breuil, Marquis de Rays, would be the rallying point.

He stood in silence, his face still illuminated by his inner vision in which he saw himself reigning over a new promised land, sovereign of the realm that had long been his dream.

It had been a long dream indeed. At the age of twenty he had exiled himself to the Far West and later his path had led to Senegal, Madagascar and Indo-China. He tried trading in all these places but, at thirty-seven, returned to France without having made his fortune and settled on his family estates in Finistère.

Living quietly in Brittany Rays contemplated his destiny. A fortuneteller had predicted he would one day be "king over a great people," but to be king he must have a kingdom and this as yet he lacked. Then he happened to read a description of New Britain, discovered by Bougainville and visited again by Duperry in 1823. While it was nominally French, no one had ever attempted to make anything of the island and Rays decided that here was the basis of his kingdom.

He brooded on his idea for several months and gradually a plan took shape. His lack of money did not disturb him, for he intended to sell land in New Britain in advance, and as for colonists, Rays was confident they would appear by the thousand, lured by the prospect of riches and adventure. For further support he counted on the Church and missionary societies. His plan was complete and the time had come to put it into practice.

"Come in, Monsieur Sumien, I was expecting you."

In interviewing a journalist from the *Gaulois* the marquis had objected to certain unfavorable articles about New Britain that had appeared in the paper's columns, and he had announced: "Nothing, nothing, do you understand, shall prevent me from accomplishing my mission, not even the petty intrigues of the government and its attempts to blacken my character and the cause I serve. I myself shall publish the truth. Next month my kingdom shall have its own newspaper, the *New France*."

It was the proof of this newspaper that its editor, Sumien, was bringing him now. Rays looked with satisfaction at the front page.

"You haven't forgotten the crest?"

"No, Monsieur le Marquis, there you see . . . 'Hope and Faith,' 'God, Freedom and Country.'"

These noble sentiments were illustrated for the subscribers' benefit by a design representing a crowd of natives converted by missionaries, some ships moored in a magnificent harbor and a town framed in the rays of the rising sun. This picture of order, industry and prosperity was emphasized by the indispensable symbols of plow, beehives, a steam engine, open books and tools.

In Sumien's files were a number of articles on such subjects as Growing Cocoa, Fishing, and How to Get On with Natives, this last accompanied by a small vocabulary of phrases in general use such as, Good morning, my friend: *Mouaourou koro malaoukou,* and Where is your house? I should like to meet your wife: *Keirouma ni ioe faifène kou.*

Other articles to appear in the columns of the *New France* were on Christopher Columbus, the discovery of Antarctica, and the great colonists.

Rays was satisfied. His latest account of investments stood at 700,000 francs, and his offices at Le Havre, Bordeaux, Marseilles and Paris were beseiged with inquiries.

"Have we any interesting recruits?" asked Rays.

They were a mixed collection including out-of-work dockers, printers, waiters, gardeners, a cooper, an accountant, and a young engineer named Alfred Capus who was to fall out at the last minute and later made a name for himself as a writer.

"We need all sorts to make a new world," said Sumien.

The marquis condescended to smile. As he was about to leave his office he was shown a list of presents, gifts from people too poor to invest in the enterprise but who wished to play some part in the common venture. They included eleven suits of clothes for the savages sewn by the young ladies of Villeneuve-les-Maguelonne "under the benevo-lent direction of Mme. Garbouleau."

"Very affecting," murmured Rays.

His plans would have been proceeding very nicely if the government had not been threatening him for "illegally raising funds," and it was no sooner established that there were no grounds for prosecution than they were bother-ing him about contravening the emigration act.

To side-step this act Rays decided his first emigrant ship, the *Chandernagor*, would be registered as an American vessel and not sail under the French flag. To prevent fur-ther eleventh-hour crises she would sail from Flushing in Holland and not from France.

At last the *Chandernagor* was ready to set sail and Rays gave a sigh of relief. Now nothing would stand in the way of the rise of New France.

The *Chandernagor* dropped anchor at Port-Breton, the future capital of the new kingdom, on January 16, 1880. The voyage had been long and uncomfortable but the emigrants had consoled themselves with the thought that they would soon be spending carefree days on the island whose luscious valleys, rich in breadfruit trees and spar-kling with waterfalls and warm beaches, already filled their imaginations.

When the *Chandernagor* sighted the island they turned in horror to Captain MacLaughlin. Could this torrid deso-lation of mud and sun-baked rocks and stunted bushes really be Port-Breton?

"The land will be what you make it," MacLaughlin told

them pitilessly. "Do you expect things to grow by themselves?"

Yet although he had never shared his passengers' optimism, he too was at bottom discouraged by the island's appearance. He circled the coast but it was the same on all sides, a mass of tumbled rocks and creepers, not without a certain magnificence but sufficiently forbidding to deter the most eager colonist. At last they settled on a creek, called by the natives Liki Liki, and landed there, though not for long. On the 20th of February, learning that the *Chandernagor* was leaving for Australia to fetch supplies, sixty of the emigrants insisted on re-embarking.

"You've not the slightest idea of perseverance," MacLaughlin stormed at them. "And that's the stuff the Marquis wants to found a kingdom with."

But the emigrants remained firm, supported by Titeu, the second-in-command.

"Very well, go," said MacLaughlin. "I shall stay here."

A month later Port-Breton faced a fresh crisis. Half of those who remained, hopeless and fever-ridden, despairing of ever making anything grow on such barren soil, decided to leave and go to the Louisiade Archipelago. "The missionaries will help us and tell us what to do," said the wretched souls.

MacLaughlin shrugged. "If you get captured by cannibals you know what to expect," he said.

Fortunately they were picked up at sea by the brig *Conflict*, which carried them to Australia.

"Now we are rid of the weak and feeble we can really get down to work," commented MacLaughlin. His words

held more obstinacy than confidence, for he knew very well that the remaining few holding out in New France would never accomplish anything.

Titeu had sent bricks from Australia but these were useless without mortar. Crops were insufficient and stores were dwindling. MacLaughlin had fifty sick on his hands, lying on improvised beds of leaves, and when his hope failed he sent them to York Island to be cared for by the missionaries.

The survivors lapsed into apathy and when, on August 25th, a British schooner anchored at Liki Liki it was MacLaughlin himself who begged the captain to take them to Australia.

All that remained of New France was a few abandoned gardens and some derelict huts.

"Gentlemen, I am happy to be able to tell you the Liberian government has made me a Commander of the Order of their country."

The Marquis de Rays flourished the insignia and his audience stared at it dutifully. They had imagined they were about to hear the latest news of New France.

"Our readers . . ." began Sumien nervously.

"You will announce this new distinction to them and at the same time point out that I am now recognized as monarch of New France by the majority of states in Europe and Africa, with the exception, of course, of republican France."

"I shall certainly do that, sir. But what news shall I give of Port-Breton?"

"You published Titeu's dispatch announcing the *Chandernagor*'s safe arrival?"

"Yes, but I think there should be more details."

"You know as well as I do that communications are slow. Make them wait."

The scene had changed from Marseilles to Barcelona, where Rays had moved the headquarters of New France in order to escape threats of prosecution, which he referred to as "intrigues." He did not allow these to disturb him; he had no need to, since his investors, who now numbered twenty thousand, still trusted him. Rays had founded a Sugar Refinery of New France at Aisne and a Farmers Co-operative Society at Nantes. A steamship, the *Genil*, was already on her way to New France and a big three-master, the *India*, was soon to sail.

When the Marquis de Rays passed the statue of Christopher Columbus on his evening walk his heart would swell with pride as he saw in himself the Christopher Columbus of a Melanesian France. For if he had not actually discovered the land, he had done better, he had colonized it, he had realized its worth and brought to birth a new, infant civilization on the distant isle.

These had been his words to Captain Rabardy of the *Genil*, who was now in sight of Port-Breton. The captain cruised up and down the deserted shore and began to have grave doubts about his abilities as a navigator. Muttering that he must be mistaken, he bent over his charts, but after checking his bearings once again he was forced to admit that the island was undoubtedly New France.

When the emigrants asked him where were the town,

the port, the other colonists, Rabardy could only shake his head helplessly. He knew no more than they. He was paid to carry them to their destination but beyond that was no concern of his.

In terrible disillusionment the emigrants wandered up and down the shore and endeavored to question the islanders about their predecessors. They found a few huts, open to the winds, unearthed some tools and returned hopelessly aboard the *Genil*. Rabardy advised them to wait for the arrival of the *India*, which was due to follow shortly. To overcome his own disappointment he visited the neighboring islands to trade with the islanders and to his astonishment found a white man among them.

"Take me with you," the wretch implored him. "My name is Boero and I am one of the emigrants from the *Chandernagor*. All my companions were massacred by savages."

Rabardy returned to Port-Breton in time to greet the arrival of the *India*. She arrived on October 14, 1880, and received an enthusiastic welcome.

Le Prévost, her captain, told Rabardy he intended taking command of the island.

"As you like," replied the other gruffly. "I shall stay on board ship where it's more comfortable."

Le Prévost put his three hundred passengers ashore, among them a doctor and a handful of missionaries. This time there were sufficient supplies, and neither medical supplies nor building materials had been forgotten. The colonists set to work eagerly but within a month their enthusiasm had slackened. There seemed no possibility of forcing a living from the barren soil and unhealthy climate.

Le Prévost announced his departure for Australia to bring back what provisions they lacked. He sailed in the *Genil*. A month, then two months passed and still she did not return. Complaining that Le Prévost had betrayed them, the colonists decided unanimously to leave the island.

On February 15th the *India* left Port-Breton for New Caledonia. Once again New France was left to the pigs rooting for food among the ruins of the settlement.

The Marquis de Rays stared furiously at his newspaper for April 10, 1881, announcing the *India*'s arrival in New Caledonia.

"It's a plot," he stormed. "A filthy plot hatched in France and carried out in Port-Breton. My subjects have been driven away from their farms. They want to destroy me. . . ."

His temper rose.

"So they want to crush my realm from the start?" he muttered. "Well, here's my answer. A fourth ship, the *New Britain*, will sail and she will be filled with brave, active men who will know how to deal with the attacks of jealous, wicked people. I shall not stoop to answer the slanders of the government press or even deny the false rumors they spread to undo my work."

Rays tore up the newspaper and addressed his colleagues. "We must consider the creation of an order of nobility for New France. I myself would suggest three classes, with perhaps a uniform. Certainly there must be some distinguishing mark, a decoration of some sort. . . ."

The Marquis de Rays sank back into his dreams.

On July 10th Rabardy, who had returned to Port-Breton with the faithful *Genil*, witnessed the arrival of the *New Britain*. She was followed by a curious vessel, an old derelict Chinese junk renamed, with unconscious irony, the *Marquis de Rays*.

"Good luck to the colonists," said Rabardy cynically.

This time the miracle happened. Within a few months a village had grown up and vegetables were growing in the painfully watered beds.

"If only we had more water," sighed the colonists.

The wish was uttered too soon, for a fortnight later the rainy season began and turned the land to a sodden river that ruined the crops. The inhabitants crouched miserably in their streaming huts and many of them came down with fever.

Tossing and turning on their beds in an atmosphere like a hothouse, the sick people believed they could hear men tramping about the village and shots ringing out in the tropical night. Baudouin, the expedition's doctor, diagnosed what he called "regional disease."

He began to fear a shortage of drugs and the *New Britain* was dispatched to Manila, to be followed soon afterward, when famine threatened, by the *Genil*.

At last on January 1st the *New Britain*'s sails appeared on the horizon, and the desperate colonists asked her captain why he had been so long in returning.

"No money had come from Barcelona," he explained. "The authorities in the Philippines wanted to put an embargo on the ship but I managed to get away during rough weather."

His face grew stern at the memory of the risks he had run. Thanks to the Marquis de Rays' negligence, he had been forced to turn pirate, but at least he could comfort himself that no one was likely to search for him on the island.

For once everyone had enough to eat. Optimism mounted higher when on January 12th the gray outline of a ship appeared off the bay. Thinking it was another shipload of colonists, the captain went out in a canoe to guide them into the bay. Watching from Port-Breton, the people saw the ship heave to and anchor about two miles off the coast.

"What is she waiting for?" they asked one another.

The night passed. At dawn the strange ship finally came into the bay and lowered a boat. In it was the unlucky captain, surrounded by armed sailors.

"The ship is a Spanish cruiser, the *Legaspi*," he explained. "I have been put under arrest for having left Manila. But they are willing to take the sick aboard."

He dared not add that the Spaniards were taking the *New Britain* as a prize.

Fate was against the wretched colonists. There were now no more than fifty of them, all utterly without hope. The *Genil* had returned but Rabardy, living aboard her with a young island girl, had lost interest in their plight.

"We can't stay where we are," said Doctor Baudouin.

By managing to sell the *Marquis de Rays* to some English traders he scraped up a little money and persuaded Ra-

bardy to take the colonists to Australia. Port-Breton was
deserted once more, and this time for good.

By the time news of the *Genil's* arrival in Australia
with the last remnants of his subjects reached the Marquis
de Rays, he was busy launching another enterprise. This
time it was not in the South Seas but in Spain, exploiting
the lead mines near Toledo. The new company would take
over, in payment of four-fifths of its shares, the assets of
New France.

"In this way my shareholders will have nothing to re-
proach me with," Rays reasoned, since their assets will
keep their value."

He had finally been compelled to admit the failure of
New France, but continued to mutter darkly about threats
and betrayals. Sumien labored to explain these to his readers. He could not ignore dispatches from Australia and
Manila when all the press was ringing with them, but he
did attempt to minimize them. He maintained that the story
of the *Legaspi's* arrival at Port-Breton was false, "at least
for the moment," and explained the colonists' departure as
the action of a handful of poor-spirited weaklings.

At the same time Sumien struggled to reassure his readers on the subject of Ray's own character. He urged them
to "take up the complete issues of this paper and reread
our articles. It will be obvious to you that the Marquis de
Rays is a man of noble and ancient race, absolutely genuine
and well intentioned, who can fitly be compared to Christopher Columbus, William Penn and Lamoricière."

But by July 15th he could no longer conceal what everyone already knew: The marquis had been arrested and extradited for swindling, lawbreaking, and manslaughter by negligence. But he still called on the last faithful few to send a message of confidence to "this noble sufferer, this new martyr to the faith." As for the investors, he announced for their comfort that "money lost in such a fashion was treasure stored up in heaven."

A number of them do not appear to have been satisfied with this consolation and the marquis was heavily sued, but the question was more than a matter of money. There were the lost and the dead to be considered, whose bones whitened on the shore of the inhospitable island.

On January 2, 1884, Rays was sentenced to four years' imprisonment and to pay three thousand francs in damages after a very able defense by his lawyers, who called him an unacknowledged prophet, persecuted and reviled, but the victim of his own folly and megalomania.

Even at this stage Rays retained some supporters to believe in his dreams.

"Wait until I am free," he told them.

But on his release from prison the king of New France, deposed before ever being crowned, retired to England where he was no doubt still seeking other islands to reign over when he died on July 29, 1894.

9

Adam and Eve and the Devil in the Galápagos Islands

O<small>N A</small> July afternoon in 1934 a small motorboat was cruising gently off Floreana, one of the smaller of the Galápagos Islands. Rounding a headland it stopped in a quiet bay screened by bushes where the sea broke softly on dark sand, and Trugve Nuggeraud left his boat and walked over to an empty barrel standing upright in the sand about a hundred yards from the sea.

The barrel was a well-known landmark to sailors, who would leave their letters in it when they passed and take out those they were able to deliver. This unique and friendly postal service worked very well although it lacked regularity, since collections were dependent on passing ships.

It was chiefly curiosity that led Trugve Nuggeraud, a Norwegian fisherman based on the islands, to look in the barrel, for there was not likely to be a letter there for him. As he was examining the envelopes he came across a folded sheet of paper with some writing on it. *I will give twenty dollars to anyone who will take me to Chatham Island,* he read. The paper was signed Lorentz.

Nuggeraud thought for a moment. The proposal interested him. Twenty dollars for a safe trip that would not take longer than forty hours was a good price and he wondered who this Lorentz was and why he wanted to leave Floreana.

For a long time Floreana had been an uninhabited island but in recent years several people had come to live there. They were a woman, Baroness Wagner, and two friends; a married couple and their son, the Wittmers; and another German couple, Friedrich and Dora Ritter.

There were strange rumors about the little colony, rumors that Nuggeraud never bothered himself to contradict although he was quite sure in his own mind that the three groups lived separately and did not get on well together.

Nuggeraud decided to earn the twenty dollars. He assumed Lorentz must be one of Baroness Wagner's friends, but as he had no idea where on the island he lived and the note carried no indication, there was nothing for it but to go and look for him. He took the small path leading into the interior of Floreana and had been walking for a little more than an hour when he suddenly stopped short in amazement.

Fifty yards away a man, naked except for a pair of boots, was pruning the branches of an orange tree. To his right spread an egg-shaped vegetable garden and farther off a little plantation of sugar cane, edged with bananas, lemon trees and pawpaws, led to a hut roofed with corrugated iron. Near this a woman, also naked, was spreading blankets in the sun.

Surprised and embarrassed, Nuggeraud walked slowly up to the man, who appeared not to have noticed his presence.

"Excuse me," said he. "But are you Lorentz?"

The man started with surprise; then, seeing the new arrival, turned and said sharply, "Can't you see we're Adam and Eve?"

Nuggeraud stared at him in perplexity, half convinced he was talking to a madman. "Adam and Eve . . . ?" he stammered.

The naked man began to laugh.

"In Germany I am called Dr. Ritter. For four years now my wife, Dora, and I have tried to live like our first parents. Won't you come into our bungalow? I don't bear you a grudge for disturbing our solitude although I don't as a rule encourage people to come. Generally when they do, they announce themselves well in advance so that we can put a few clothes on. . . . You are looking for Lorentz, did you say? I'm afraid we don't see anything of him but I can tell you where you may find him."

Friedrich Ritter was forty-three and a successful Berlin doctor when he and his wife Dora embarked on the *Boskop* at Amsterdam on July 4, 1929, bound for the Galápagos Islands.

He had long dreamed of living on a desert island where

he would find solitude, independence, peace of mind, and the leisure to cultivate a capacity for meditation. He was a man of wide reading and had been deeply impressed by the story of Robinson Crusoe, feeling that his life would have lacked something if he never lived as Defoe's hero had done. Ritter had waited twenty years to realize his dream and at last set off, turning his back without regret on his comfortable house and practice.

Among the fifty-odd islands of the Galápagos he had finally, after much thought, settled on Floreana, once the stronghold of the pirates Morgan and Dampier, which the Norwegians had already tried unsuccessfully to colonize. The choice was a good one. Floreana has an equable climate, the temperature is constant and, even more important, the soil is fertile. "It will be an earthly paradise," Ritter had declared, developing ambitions to add the role of Adam to that of Crusoe.

A few days were enough to dispel some of his illusions. Clouds of mosquitoes demonstrated the usefulness of clothes, and his lack of experience in primitive life led to many mistakes.

Building a hut proved more difficult than they had anticipated, especially making and putting on a roof. Ritter finally gave up the attempt and they were forced to take shelter in the lava caves, which were unbearable by day because of the hot sun. At last the skipper of a passing Norwegian ship gave them the corrugated iron for a roof and the hut was finished.

Slowly they developed their way of life. The first crops from the garden provided them with sufficient food, for they were vegetarians, and Ritter was able to devote himself to his favorite pastime of meditation.

The solitary life encourages thought. Robinson Crusoe's inner life is not purely a literary invention of Defoe's, for the examples of Selkirk and Serrano show that solitude has led even the most inarticulate to prayer; their discovery of God being perhaps no more than the effect of prolonged loneliness driving them to seek higher protection.

Naturally such a leaning was stronger in a man of Ritter's character who had set out from the first to cultivate a capacity for meditation.

But although Ritter knelt and kissed the ground in the first moments of exaltation after taking possession of his retreat, he soon realized his paradise presented certain inconveniences, even for a philosopher.

The thinker needs silence above all, but a shattering cacophony rose about the Ritter's cabin, especially at night when the anguished bray of wild donkeys was answered by lowing cattle, grunting pigs and the frenetic uproar of cat and dog fights. A wild boar trampled the garden and plantations during the night, creating such havoc that, despite his horror of killing, Ritter was forced to shoot at it.

Failing to hit the creature with his gun, Ritter tried dynamite. For several nights on end the island echoed to his deafening explosions but the boar was not among the victims and its depredations continued.

Ritter gave up with the philosophic thought that the devil was bound to find his way into the garden of Eden and, reflecting with resignation that heaven and hell were both realms of the spirit, he noted in his journal a quotation from Nietzsche: "It must be the best of all possible worlds, for if it were better it would be heaven."

Ritter soon abandoned all notions of a garden of Eden and consoled himself with the reflection that Adam and Eve benefited by being expelled from paradise in the discovery of the joys of honest toil and spiritual peace and love.

Yet his plan was far from a failure on material grounds. His farming flourished and he managed to live without any outside help. This relative success was one of the reasons for the drama that was to burst on Floreana.

Various journalists visited the "Robinsons of the Galápagos" and as a result of their articles Ritter received numerous letters in the barrel at Post Office Bay from people who wished to join him; offers which he immediately declined. It was exactly its isolation which gave a meaning to his life and he would not have encouraged the company of strangers for anything in the world.

However, he could not prevent one couple, the Wittmers, from settling on Floreana with their fifteen-year-old son. The boy suffered from TB and his parents hoped a natural life would restore ther child's health. This family's relations with the Ritters were no more than neighborly, but no discord troubled their association. With Baroness Wagner things were to be different.

Friedrich and Dora Ritter were resting in their hut one morning in May 1933 when they heard steps on the path. Ritter stood up and went to the window, where he saw a woman of about forty accompanied by two men.

"I am Baroness Wagner," she introduced herself, "and these gentlemen are Mr. Lorentz and Mr. Philipson. I'm very pleased to meet you, Dr. Ritter. All the papers have been full of your marvelous life here on Floreana and so I have decided to come and share in it."

Ritter listened to her expressionlessly.

"Share my life? What do you mean by that?"

"Dr. Ritter, I think we should start a community whose members would follow the same rules of life, perform the same work—"

"Madam," Ritter interrupted dryly, "what I sought on Floreana was above all else peace, and your offer does not have the slightest appeal to me."

"But—"

"In the four years I have been settled on Floreana I have never felt the least wish for the company of my fellow men."

Turning his back on her Ritter returned to his interrupted meditations.

Baroness Wagner was not to be put off so easily, having once made up her mind to settle on Floreana, although her only desire was not, as she had told Ritter, to lead a healthy, natural life. Before embarking for the island she had announced her intention of opening a hotel for millionaires who wanted to play at being Robinson Crusoes. The ship that had brought her to Floreana had also brought building materials for the purpose.

Baroness Wagner settled in the north of the island at the foot of a volcanic peak rising nearly two thousand feet above sea level. There, with the help of Philipson, an

American, and the German Lorentz, she began work on her hotel, which she named Hotel Paradise.

As Ritter saw nothing of the baroness for some time, he assumed she had left the island, when one afternoon she reappeared and told him: "I have come to let you know I have built a hotel and it is now ready to be opened. Soon a great many people will be landing on Floreana. Here is what the newspapers say about my plans."

She held out to Ritter a sheaf of press cuttings stating that Floreana, the "enchanted isle," was to become the refuge of all those who were tired of modern life, and praising Baroness Wagner for devoting herself to the regeneration of her contemporaries.

"If you would like a share in my profits," offered the baroness, "I will make you medical superintendent of my colony."

Ritter angrily declined her offer. He believed she was mad and cursed the woman who had come to disturb his solitude with her crowds of tourists who would rush all over the island organizing hunting parties and boating trips. His paradise would become pandemonium.

"Not only do I refuse," he told her, "but I warn you I shall do everything in my power to make the strangers leave. Moreover, you must be well aware you can't feed or house them and they will be thoroughly uncomfortable here."

The Baroness retorted that nothing would prevent her from carrying out her plans, and departed, leaving Ritter fuming and declaring the woman was unbalanced, a megalomaniac, an unsuccessful adventuress making one last bid for notoriety.

Certainly Baroness Wagner made every effort to gain publicity. One of her stunts was to order twenty thousand cases of Camel cigarettes from the manufacturers to be sent to Baroness Wagner, Empress of the Galápagos Islands. But the Empress reigned over only two subjects, Philipson and Lorentz. The expected millionaires never came, although she redoubled her statements to the press, which were dispatched by passing ships as well as by the tramp steamer that visited the islands every two months.

Disappointment made her change her methods. Instead of advertising a return to nature she started encouraging strange stories about the island, to attract customers, and these were seized on eagerly by the sensational weeklies. The Empress of the Galápagos figured as a present-day Circe who drew men to her island and then kept them there, and photographs were published of her taking a ship by storm. Rumors began to circulate that Floreana was the wickedest island and every imaginable vice was said to be practiced there.

This brought a few yachts cruising in the vicinity but had their crews landed, instead of contenting themselves with raking the island's shores with binoculars, they would have found only an idealist cultivating his garden and philosophizing, a peaceable elderly couple watching over their child's health, and three unhappy people leading their sordid lives in an atmosphere of jealousy and suspicion punctuated by the hysterical outbursts of a woman who could neither forget a past when she was the talk of Paris, nor leave her dreams of the fame and luxury ahead, which in her saner moments she knew would never come true.

One or two guests eventually arrived at the Hotel Paradise but they soon left. Slowly the legend of Baroness Wagner, the Circe of the Galápagos, fell apart. Refusing to admit defeat, she vented her ill temper on Lorentz, who had been replaced by Philipson as the favorite of the moment. To escape from her tyranny for a few hours Lorentz developed the habit of visiting his nearest neighbors, the peacable Wittmers.

One morning in January 1934 he arrived, as he did several times a week, at the Wittmers' house.

"Still no guests?" Wittmer asked him.

"I can't go on like this. I've had all I can stand."

Wittmer had sensed for a long time that all was not well between Baroness Wagner, Philipson and Lorentz, without being sure whether the trouble lay in rivalry between the two men or in quarrels among three people all blaming each other for the failure of their venture.

"I've had enough," repeated Lorentz.

"Why?" asked Wittmer.

Lorentz replied by a strange request.

"May I come and live here for a little while?"

"Live here?"

"Yes. Until I can find a boat to take me to the mainland. I'm desperate. You can't refuse me this."

Lorentz seemed on the edge of a physical and mental breakdown. He clung to Wittmer's hand until Wittmer gently freed himself.

"Certainly," he said, feeling a sudden rush of pity for Lorentz. "You may stay as long as you like."

Lorentz sat down, his shoulders sagging, and muttered, "I'll get back at them."

176

"Get back at them for what?"

He was silent for a moment, holding his head in his hands, then as if talking to himself he went on in broken phrases. "I can't stay there any longer. . . . Let them get on as they can, perhaps that would be my best revenge after all. . . . I've had enough of this miserable island. . . . I've had enough. . . ."

Temporarily giving up all idea of finding out what had taken place at Hotel Paradise, Wittmer offered Lorentz a hut to sleep in, and the German spent the whole day lying in it. Wittmer expected the Baroness to come looking for him but no one appeared. When Lorentz was himself once more he volunteered no information about why he had left the hotel and Wittmer made no attempt to question him, hoping he would reveal the truth of his own accord.

The third day after his arrival at the Wittmers' Lorentz suddenly announced he was going up to the hotel for a few hours.

"I'll be back this evening," he said.

It was dusk before he walked up the path leading to the Wittmers' cabin, carrying a heavy suitcase. He seemed tired.

"It's all over," he told Wittmer. "The baroness and her friend are leaving as I told you they would. An English yacht is picking them up tomorrow evening."

"An English yacht? When did it arrive? I was at the bay yesterday and there was nothing there."

"It must have moored in the north of the island."

"I'm surprised because I've seen nobody. Generally when ships call at Floreana the crews take the opportunity to see the island."

"I didn't find anyone at Hotel Paradise, either," said Lorentz.

"Not even the baroness?"

"Oh yes, of course. I saw her and Philipson. They seemed highly delighted at the prospect of leaving. Between you and me, I think they'd been drinking."

"That wouldn't surprise me. But tell me, if you mean to leave Floreana, don't you want to take advantage of the yacht yourself?"

Lorentz's face set.

"With them? Definitely not. I shall leave a letter in the barrel at Post Office Bay. I'll soon find a boat to take me far away from here, and from them."

Lorentz retired to his hut still carrying the case. Wittmer noticed it must be very heavy, for he had to stop and rest twice although the distance was only fifty yards.

Next morning Lorentz said to his host. "You didn't notice anything during the night?"

"What sort of thing?"

"I couldn't sleep and took a turn outside. I heard voices in the distance, speaking English, and footsteps and shouting and, I thought, a sound like an anchor being taken up."

"The yacht you mentioned?"

"Apparently."

"You told me she did not sail until tonight."

"I suppose either the owner or Baroness Wagner was in a hurry for some reason. Anyway they're off my mind. I'm going up to the hotel now. See you this evening."

Lorentz walked away.

That afternoon Wittmer was tempted to go up to the

Hotel Paradise himself, but he was content to go to the
bay where ships generally anchored. It was empty. When
he returned it was fairly late and Lorentz was already
home.

"It's just as I said," Lorentz said. "The Baroness and
Philipson have gone. The hotel is empty."

"Don't you think there's something funny about such a
sudden departure?"

"If you knew the baroness as well as I do, nothing she
did would surprise you."

"I walked as far as the bay this afternoon but I saw no
sign of a yacht."

"Because I told you they sailed last night."

Lorentz's voice was slightly raised and he sounded
strained and nervous.

"Of course," Wittmer responded simply.

He was certain something had occurred and that Lorentz knew more about it than he would admit but for
some private reason he preferred to keep quiet.

In the next few days Lorentz made several visits to the
Hotel Paradise and returned with an assortment of objects,
including bedding, chairs and cooking utensils, and these
he sold to Wittmer or Dr. Ritter. Then he left his letter in
the barrel at Post Office Bay asking for a boat to take him
to Chatham Island.

He waited a month, two months, and when he was not
helping Wittmer in his work he spent his time watching
for ships. Several called for a few hours at the island and
every time Lorentz went aboard asking for a passage to
Chatham Island, but was always refused because it lay off

the ship's course. Various captains offered to take him to
Ecuador, the United States and even to Europe, but Lorentz insisted on Chatham, the largest of the Galápagos Islands. He would never explain his reasons, even to Wittmer.

On July 13th in the middle of the afternoon a man of
about thirty suddenly appeared in front of the bungalow.

"Are you Mr. Lorentz?" he asked Wittmer.

"No. What do you want him for?"

"My name is Nuggeraud. I found a note from Mr. Lorentz asking to be taken to Chatham Island. Dr. Ritter
told me he was living with you."

"Quite right. I'll go and find him. He'll be so glad you
can do this for him; he's been trying to leave Floreana for
so long."

Five minutes later Lorentz appeared.

"Can you really take me to Chatham?" he asked Nuggeraud, like a child not daring to believe his dream was
coming true.

"I think I may be able to. Are you offering twenty dollars?"

"Twenty dollars. It's a deal. Give me a quarter of an
hour to pack my things and I'll be ready."

"Do you want to leave at once?" asked Nuggeraud in
surprise.

"Of course."

Wittmer stared at Lorentz. It almost looked as though he
were scared of something.

"Excuse me," said Nuggeraud. "Would you mind waiting until tomorrow?"

"Wait? What for? It's a fine day, the sea's calm. . . ."

"It's not that." Nuggeraud hesitated a moment before going on. "It's because of the date."

Wittmer and Lorentz looked at each other without understanding.

"Today's the thirteenth. It's not good to sail on Friday the thirteenth."

Lorentz seemed to breathe again. If that was the only difficulty. . . .

"You don't really believe such nonsense?" he said.

"It brings bad luck," repeated Nuggeraud obstinately. "All the sailors say so."

"Listen," said Lorentz. "I have already waited a long time. It is very important to me to leave this island as soon as possible. Please, will you go today?"

Wittmer was watching the German and saw that his voice and movements had become jerky and tense.

"It must be urgent," said the bewildered fisherman, who could see no reason for such haste.

"It is. Let's go," said Lorentz grimly.

He fetched his two heavy suitcases, said good-by to Mrs. Wittmer, shook her husband's hand warmly and then led the way rapidly down the path leading to the bay.

Two hours later he was aboard the *Dynamita* urging Nuggeraud to sail, as though he feared he would change his mind. He allowed him only enough time to fill a water cask and pick some fruit.

The outboard motor coughed in the stillness and the boat's wake curved out toward the sea, already turning leaden gray in the approaching night.

After Lorentz had departed peace returned to Floreana. Adam and Eve continued their philosophizing and the Wittmers, relieved of their guest, resumed their quiet existence.

But Wittmer often thought about Baroness Wagner's strange disappearance. Convinced there was some mystery and searching for the answer, he climbed up to the Hotel Paradise and found it wrecked and littered with empty packing cases. The building was already falling to ruin and the roof had fallen in in several places.

Wittmer felt strangely oppressed as he examined the pathetic remains of the derelict paradise. He thought about Lorentz's silence, which he found both interesting and disturbing. That the German had not wished to explain his quarrel with Baroness Wagner might be perfectly reasonable, although not to give a reason for his flight from the Hotel Paradise was less so, but if he had been lying about the way in which the baroness had left the island, that was disturbing indeed.

Lorentz must surely have been hiding something from me, thought Wittmer. But the truth is bound to come out sooner or later. The baroness will be talked about in Guayaquil, where she has most likely gone.

When the boat from Ecuador visited the islands and called at Floreana, Wittmer questioned her captain.

"No, we haven't seen Baroness Wagner in Guayaquil," was the reply. "We thought she was still here."

The news of the "Empress's" disappearance spread rapidly and journalists began to arrive in Floreana. They visited the ruins of the Hotel Paradise, feeling, like Wittmer, that something strange had happened there without being able to draw any further conclusions.

Several months went by and there was no trace of the baroness in Chile, Brazil, America or Europe. Suddenly on November 20th her name appeared again on the front page of the papers.

This time she had not settled on another island. A Spanish ship had found the bodies of two people beside an abandoned boat at Marchena, a sandy islet among the Galápagos. The bodies were in an advanced stage of decay, almost reduced to skeletons. It was at first thought they were those of the baroness and Philipson.

Allen Hancock, the owner of a large motor yacht which had made several cruises in the Galápagos, who knew Baroness Wagner well, had a different opinon. His theory was that the bodies were those of the Wittmer family.

"Why should they have left Floreana?" people asked.

"I don't know. Only I'd be very surprised if the bodies turned out to be Baroness Wagner and her friend."

Hancock seemed sure of his ground and fresh information from the islands proved him partly right. A French passport bearing the name Alfred Rudolph Lorentz, 211 Avenue Daumesnil, Paris, had been found on one of the bodies. The two unfortunates who had died at Marchena were Lorentz and Trugve Nuggeraud.

The facts of their death remain a mystery. The boat had been run up the beach, intact and in perfect running order, so that there could be no question of a shipwreck. It was assumed that the *Dynamita*'s motor must have failed and Nuggeraud had put in to Marchena to repair it but had not succeeded and the two men had died of thirst on the deserted islet well away from shipping routes.

In Lorentz's pocket investigators found a letter addressed in his own handwriting to Allen Hancock, telling him of his wish to leave the island where he hinted in veiled terms a terrible scandal had occurred.

The mystery of Floreana can be summed up as follows: One evening Baroness Wagner and Philipson disappeared. Lorentz declared they boarded an English yacht, which nobody saw. Nothing more was heard of them, but four months later Lorentz himself was found dead on a desert island.

The points detectives wished to clear up were whether the baroness had really left the island on a yacht and, if so, why all attempts to find her had failed, and why Lorentz had not left with her, and what was the cause of their quarrel.

At first it was thought the much-disputed yacht had been Allen Hancock's, but when detectives questioned him he repeated that, although he knew Baroness Wagner, she had never asked him to help her leave Floreana.

"When the two bodies were found, and before their identity was proved, you asserted they could not be those of the baroness and Philipson. Why?"

"Because I knew she was not crazy enough to embark at random in a small boat."

"How do you explain the letter found on Lorentz and addressed to you?"

"He must have thought of me when he considered ways

of leaving the island. He left a letter in the barrel at Post Office Bay and before getting into Nuggeraud's boat took back his letter which had no further use."

While Hancock was being questioned, police also landed on Floreana. They visited Dr. Ritter's bungalow intending to take a statement from him, but found he had died a short while before. His wife said they had not seen the baroness for a long time. In her opinion, she had committed suicide.

"And the story about going aboard a yacht?"

"That was to save face."

"But surely the corpses would have been found?"

"Not if they had thrown themselves into the sea."

"Why should she have wanted to hide her death?"

Dora Ritter shrugged.

"How can you tell with people like her?" And she added in tones of dislike, "That woman brought bad luck to Floreana. She was the devil incarnate."

The police also went to see Wittmer, who said only Lorentz knew the truth.

"He didn't give anything away when he lived with you?"

"Nothing of any interest."

"Didn't you think his silence strange?"

"Certainly I did."

"Do you think the baroness and Philipson committed suicide?"

"I think Lorentz would have told me if they had."

"Supposing they had died on the island and Lorentz knew but had not told you. What conclusions would you draw?"

185

"It's not my business to draw conclusions."

Wittmer realized the police were suggesting Lorentz might have murdered his two companions and disposed of their bodies by throwing them in the sea. This would explain his silence, his obvious anxiety, his desire to leave the island as quickly as possible and go, not to the mainland, but to Chatham Island where he would feel safe from the police. But a motive had to be found for the crime, if crime there was. Jealousy and mental disturbance were suggested; then a policeman produced another theory: gain.

There was a legend of buried treasure on Floreana, as there is on so many pirate islands, although neither the Ritters nor the Wittmers were interested in it. But the "Empress of the Galápagos" had been heard to refer to it more than once in front of journalists, and while buried treasure would make a substantial addition to her publicity, it was not impossible she had discovered it by chance. If so Lorentz could have rid himself of the baroness and Philipson, stolen the treasure and fled. Wittmer had undoubtedly seen the German with a heavy suitcase he could scarcely carry and this might have contained the treasure. The suitcase had mysteriously vanished. The Spanish skipper who found the bodies did not mention it.

The police could only wait and wonder. There was no proof of Lorentz's crime and it was even possible that one day the eccentric baroness would appear again to disprove it.

But the name of the ex-Empress of the Galápagos remained shrouded in mystery.

Dora Ritter went back to Germany and wrote a book,

aimed at the baroness, which she called *And the Devil Came Into the Garden.*

Today, after being temporarily occupied by the Americans during the war, Floreana is again a peaceful island. Its only inhabitants are an exiled revolutionary named Luis Martinez, a small garrison, and Wittmer, whose family has now grown to five. In his mind there are still memories of undiscovered tragedies and a lost paradise.

was a dream, Lovey, a bad nasty dream but Daddy's here and you're safe in my arms once again."

Later that night he showed her the tape.

It was as if he had branded her.

She was his to do with as he pleased.

So in a final act of perversion . . . he married her.

"Nice shooting, Lovey," Jack said when he came into the room. "So don't be crazy-assed, you know, put down the gun."

She looked at him wildly, ready to take a few more with her, ready to take them all. Gennaro, Bernie, the Japanese, and Jack . . . she had a bul-let for each and every one.

"Lovey . . . ?" said Jack, smiling his Wolfey grin.

"Lovey, you hungry? Shall I send out for some-thing? We can clean up the mess later. Come on, Lovey, we go for oysters."

They left the dead guy on the floor and went to the Mirage. Jack tried to talk to her into seeing Siegfried and Roy.

"I love those two fairies with the tigers," he said. "Come on, Lovey, you've never seen the white tigers? The dead guy is not going anywhere, that's why they call him dead."

At about the time that Siegfried was joyously plunging sabers into an enraptured Roy, strapped down spread eagle in basic studs and wet black leather, Jack got up and said, "Excuse me, Lovey, I've got to go and drain my lizard."

By the time they got back, the dead guy was gone. The carpet was shampooed, the wall was spackled, and there were flowers. Lilies. Someone had a sense of humor.

Nora was amazed . . . impressed . . . grateful and afraid; all the emotions that Jack treasured.

"One phone call does it all, Lovey," he sang. "It